ADHESIVE BONDING

ALCOA ALUMINUM

ADHESIVE BONDING

ALCOA ALUMINUM

ALUMINUM COMPANY OF AMERICA
PITTSBURGH, PA.

TABLE OF CONTENTS

INTRODUCTION

WHY ADHESIVES ADHERE

ON HISTORIC EVIDENCE, the use of glues and cements is almost as old as mankind itself—adhesive bonding is indeed an ancient art. In recent decades, it has become a highly developed technology utilizing many scientific disciplines. Yet, despite its widely accepted status as a reliable industrial tool, adhesive bonding may not be considered a full-fledged science—for the data in this field are largely empirical and the explanations are still, to some degree, speculative.

For example, in two and one-half centuries we have been unable to proceed much beyond Sir Isaac Newton's unsophisticated description of the phenomena of adhesion. In 1704, he wrote of "Agents in Nature able to make the Particles of Bodies stick together by very strong Attractions."

Several of the current theories that attempt to explain the forces causing adhesion are contradictory in some respects and vague in others. There is one inescapable conclusion: We don't yet know precisely why adhesives adhere; basic theories remain to be proved.

Despite the lack of a unified theory, large-scale practical advances have been made, such as the development of high-strength adhesives—notably epoxy and phenolic resins. These can now be used to bond virtually all known solids, often achieving higher efficiency and lower costs than are possible with other joining methods. With the development of new adhesives, the technology of adhesive-bonding aluminum—to itself and to other metals or nonmetallics—has attained widespread acceptance.

Since Alcoa's chief concern is to help its customers in the best possible utilization of aluminum and its alloys, the company maintains an active interest in research and development in the field of adhesive bonding. This is in keeping with Alcoa's policies on all aspects of aluminum technology—from the primary production of metal through forming, fabricating, joining and finishing.

This book serves as a useful reference that will give aluminum users the most current information on adhesive-joining techniques. Conceived as a broad, objective review of the art, *Adhesive Bonding Alcoa Aluminum** will aid the reader in making realistic preliminary appraisals of adhesive-bonding applications for his own production plans.

It should be noted that this publication is a generalized assessment of possibilities inherent in adhesive-bonding techniques — a guide to be used at the preparatory stage of evaluation.

The adhesive compositions and joint designs mentioned in the text should not be considered as specific or definitive recommendations. Many variables influence the performance of a particular adhesive-bonded joint, and only direct analysis of each problem by competent professionals can give the proper answers for a given application. Alcoa's technical representative and those of reputable manufacturers of adhesives should be called upon to help deal with specific problems.

When considering applications of adhesive bonding to aluminum, it will pay you to consult Alcoa—your best source of information regarding all aspects of aluminum technology.

---

* It should be recognized that to anticipate every condition of application and use would be beyond the capacity of any materials producer. Aluminum Company of America, therefore, disclaims any responsibility or liability for designs based on the information included in this book.

Adhesive-bonded aluminum lighting standards on a major New York City highway.

Chapter 1

SOME APPLICATIONS
OF ADHESIVE-BONDED JOINTS

ADHESIVE BONDING is more than a mere substitute for other joining techniques. It has inherent characteristics that make it especially valuable for a great number of applications in cases where other methods cannot be used, or where it has proved its superiority.

One immediately apparent advantage is the inconspicuousness of an adhesive-bonded joint; in some instances it is practically invisible. This, of course, is an important factor where product appearance must be considered. Adhesives provide not only a method of joining, but also perform the function of a sealant.

The continuous contact between two bonded surfaces may be structurally significant because it can provide a more evenly distributed load than would be obtainable with other joining methods.

Adhesive joints can afford protection against the galvanic corrosion that often occurs when dissimilar metals are joined.

Applications described in this book are concerned with actual or potential adhesive-bonding developments. The following listing is necessarily incomplete; Alcoa's intent here is to indicate the scope of existing possibilities.

Fig. 1—An impregnated-paper honeycomb core frequently used in aluminum-faced structural sandwich panels.

Adhesives are used increasingly for joining aluminum products such as sheet, extrusions, tube, structural shapes, foil, plate, wire, rod, bar, forgings and castings. Adhesive-bonding technology has progressed to the point where adhesives, in some cases, offer structural advantages over other methods of joining—such as welding, riveting and bolting. For example, it is possible to maintain full inherent properties when aluminum adherends are joined by an adhesive. Welding tends to reduce these properties in the heat-affected zone. Adhesives also make it possible to combine aluminum with other materials and, thus, sometimes provide the only means of joining—as will be illustrated in some of these applications. No attempt has been made to list all adhesive-bonding applications that are used, or can be used, in the fabrication of aluminum products; what follows is a fairly representative group of examples.

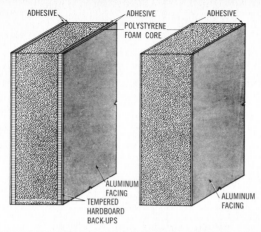

Fig. 2—Attractive Alcoa* Alply Panels have a foamed-plastic core that is adhesive-bonded to aluminum facings. Alply Panels are also available with hardboard backing.

Building Products

Structural sandwich panels represent what is probably the most common use for structural adhesives.

Aluminum facings can be made to adhere to core materials, such as aluminum or paper honeycomb, to give a high composite strength-to-weight ratio. Adhesives with filleting properties are required for honeycomb cores. A modified phenolic is often used with aluminum honeycomb for high strength, while a neoprene or nitrile-based organic-solvent type of adhesive is often used with impregnated-paper honeycomb. Epoxy adhesives are also used in the fabrication of sandwich panels.

Aluminum facings—or facings of aluminum laminated to backup materials such as hardboard or plywood—may be combined with a variety of core materials of plastics, woods or metals. The adhesive

* Registered Trademarks of Aluminum Company of America.

must transmit shear stress from the facings to the core. It must also be able to resist the tendency of the thin aluminum facings to buckle under design loads or under thermal stresses caused by variations in the panel components' coefficients of thermal expansion.

Aluminum-faced panels with foamed plastic cores, such as Alcoa * Alply Panels, can be used as structural, insulating and decorative elements. Adhesives are chosen that will develop the full strength of the panel core. A panel of this type has a very high strength-to-weight ratio. Shear stress in the core may be reduced by using thicker cores, thereby getting better stiffness, stability and insulating properties in the finished unit.

Sandwich panel applications can be found in nearly every industry, either as building components or as equipment enclosures for heating and/or cooling units. Sandwich panels permit covering large areas with flat aluminum facing materials. Fig. 2 shows a cutaway of this kind of panel. Panels also provide a convenient way to insulate openings. A common application of this type is a spandrel panel in an aluminum grid-type curtain wall, as shown in Fig. 3a. Sandwich panels may also be used to enclose entire buildings, as shown in Figs. 3b and 3c.

Alcoa Insulated Horizontal Siding is another aluminum product that utilizes adhesives. In this product, foamed polystyrene beadboard is laminated to preformed, prepainted aluminum siding. Other siding products have been fabricated by laminating aluminum, having a durable baked-paint finish, to wood-base materials. Many kinds of colored and embossed aluminum foil have been laminated to a variety of nonmetallic substrates for general decorative purposes. Thin aluminum foil is also laminated to plywood, hardboard, gypsum board, paper, etc., to provide a reflective surface and/or a vapor barrier which is desirable when these porous materials are used on the warm side of an insulated wall.

Foil-to-paper laminates are also used extensively as vapor barrier facings or enclosures for roll- or batt-type fibrous insulation. Other uses include the combining of such laminates with a variety of materials to provide a foil-clad sheathing material.

In the building products field, cast aluminum is often used as decorative paneling both for interior and exterior walls, and for stair railings, fireplaces, etc. Adhesives can replace the various mechanical fasteners and other joining methods presently used to

---

* Registered Trademarks of Aluminum Company of America

Fig. 3a—Phoenix Mutual Insurance Company, Hartford, Conn.

Fig. 3b—Otis Elevator Company Plant, Bloomington, Ill.

Fig. 3c—Three Rivers Storage Co., Pittsburgh, Pa.

Fig. 4—A modified epoxy adhesive was used to provide the strong permanent bond between the aluminum plaque and the plate glass.

mount such paneling on aluminum, steel, wood and other kinds of permanent structures.

There is a wide variety of miscellaneous uses for structural adhesives in such diverse areas as window frames, insect-screen frames, and attachment of hardware in aluminum-faced, flush-panel doors.

Items now cast as single units around disposable core material may be made by suitable adhesive-bonding of a few relatively simple cast shapes—with little or no coring. Cast aluminum letters can be adhesive-bonded to standard cast or wrought backgrounds, as in plaques or markers.

Fig. 5—Aluminum extrusions bonded to aluminum sheets are used for highway sign panels.

Structures

Aluminum highway structures and products are being created, utilizing structural adhesives to connect tubular parts in sign structures and lighting standards and to join composite products made up of sheet and extrusions. Aluminum-faced sandwich panels are currently being used for large road signs.

Alcoa has helped develop new types of sign panels and sign and light standards as adhesive-bonded structures (see Figs. 5 and 6), all of improved and more versatile design.

Aluminum or wood seats and backs can be bonded to cast aluminum stadium-seat supports.

Fig. 6—In extruded light standards, used on major highways, the pole is adhesive-bonded into the cast aluminum base, as shown in the cutaway.

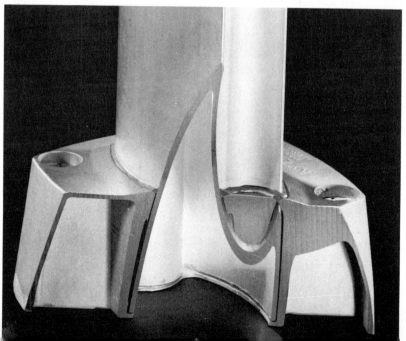

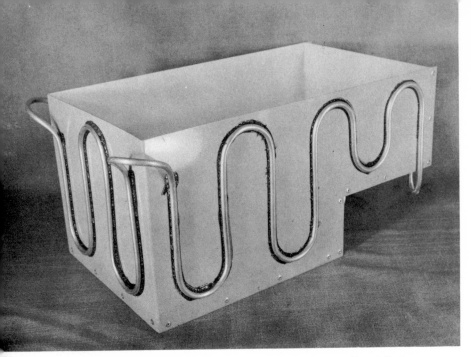

Fig. 7—Aluminum tubing joined to a prototype refrigerator liner with an adhesive.

Appliances

To approach the highly competitive market in various cast components—for example, washer pumps and vending-equipment dispensing units—adhesives can be used to bond relatively inexpensive castings. Adhesives can also be used to join aluminum fittings to housings of either aluminum or dissimilar material.

Aluminum tubing can be joined with adhesives in fabricating aluminum air-conditioner and refrigeration-unit coils (see Fig. 7). Although these and many other parts could also be brazed or soldered, the use of adhesives eliminates the flux requirement.

Adhesives are used in joining spirally wound foil fins to copper tubing (see Fig. 8). This aluminum-to-copper fin-tubing heat-exchanger assembly is made by slipping the spirally wound aluminum fin over regular copper tubing and securing it in place with a low-viscosity 100 percent solids paste adhesive of the modified epoxy type.

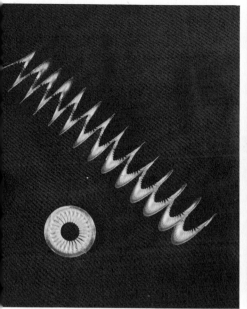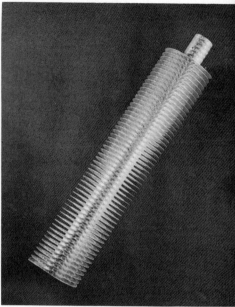

Fig. 8—An aluminum-to-copper fin-tubing heat-exchanger using a spiral aluminum fin over copper tubing.

Fig. 9—Prototype of an aluminum refrigerator tray in which nylon-modified epoxy film was used to bond the angles to the perforated and corrugated sheets.

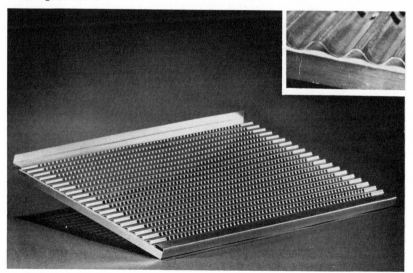

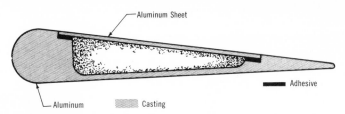

Fig. 10—Sectional view of a cast aluminum hydrofoil used to surround an outboard motor propeller to increase its effective pulling power. An aluminum sheet was adhesive-bonded to the aluminum casting.

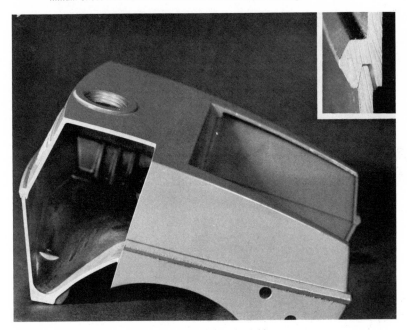

Fig. 11—Cutaway section of the gasoline tank for a portable power saw, which shows two aluminum die castings bonded with a one-part epoxy paste. An enlarged detail of the joint configuration is depicted in the inset.

Sporting Equipment

One company is making a cast-aluminum hydrofoil to surround the propeller of an outboard motor, thereby increasing the effective pulling power. To produce this part, a sheet of aluminum is adhesive-bonded to the periphery of a permanent-mold casting (see Fig. 10). Other possible applications on outboard motors include bonded cover panels, gas tanks, oil tanks, and steel ring gears to aluminum flywheels.

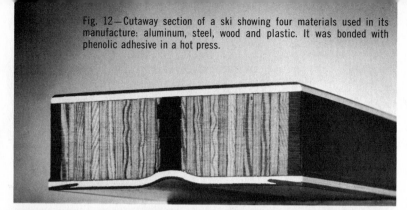

Fig. 12—Cutaway section of a ski showing four materials used in its manufacture: aluminum, steel, wood and plastic. It was bonded with phenolic adhesive in a hot press.

Fig. 13—Prototype model of a bicycle using aluminum tubing adhesive-bonded to aluminum castings.

Seaworthy cast aluminum boat-trim decorations, such as lights and standards, can be adhesive-bonded to aluminum boats, as well as to boats constructed of other materials. Castings can be bonded to aluminum tubing, sheet and other structural elements to make ladders, railings and the like for swimming pools, docks, boats, etc.

Snow skis and water skis are fabricated of aluminum and other materials using adhesive-bonding techniques (see Fig. 12).

Fig. 14—To manufacture rotor end plates for air motors—such as are used in portable pneumatic tools—a high-strength thermosetting film adhesive (center) makes the bond between a powdered iron disc (left) and a die-cast aluminum plate (right). The finished bond is so strong that the powdered metal component will fail, under stressing, before the adhesive joint gives way.

Process Industries

Adhesives are widely used in the process industries to simplify the development of prototype equipment.

Of particular interest in this industrial area is the possibility of bonding wear and bearing surfaces to aluminum and dissimilar materials. The bonding of aluminum bearing material to an aluminum or steel backing plate can be used for gear pumps, hydraulic-valve spools, etc. Wear plates have been adhesive-bonded to components of equipment for materials handling, and for water pumps and similar equipment, to achieve lightweight units with proper wear characteristics.

Identification tags can be bonded to mechanical equipment, thus eliminating the need for rivets and other mechanical fasteners now in use.

Structural connections of aluminum pipe and tube are being developed through the use of high-strength modified epoxy adhesives. One application involves an aluminum pipe with a modified-epoxy joint, to be used in gas-gathering service.

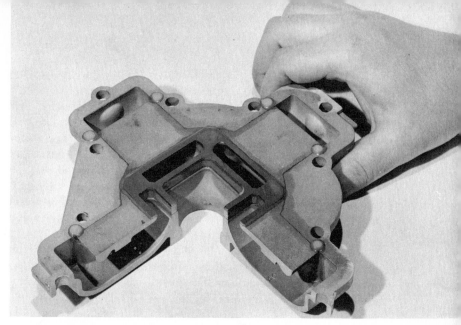

Fig. 15—The cutaway portion of a pump assembly reveals its three adhesive-bonded die-cast sections.

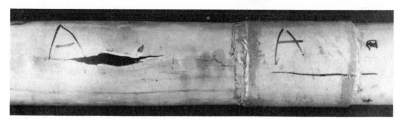

Fig. 16—The sleeve joint of this pipe assembly was bonded with a one-part epoxy adhesive. In a hydrostatic test, failure occurred outside of the joint.

Fig. 17—A number of complex die castings are adhesive-bonded to produce this intake manifold.

Automotive

Chassis — The growing use of aluminum in the automotive field, for engines as well as a variety of other items (trim, rocker arms, transmission cases, brake drums and the like), makes it likely that many other conversions from ferrous materials will take place in the near future. In the development of a rear-axle housing, one problem was to find a suitable method of attaching the steel axle tube to the aluminum housing. Adhesives offer a good solution.

Adhesive bonding of steel wear plates to aluminum suspension parts and V-belt drive sheaves can satisfy the need to make a good, lightweight unit with satisfactory wear characteristics.

An adhesive has also been used to provide an airtight seal and to retain a core plug in an air-ride saddle truck-suspension system.

Engine Components — Alcoa and several engine manufacturers are giving considerable attention to the use of adhesives for bonding die-cast or full permanent-mold castings in place of a semipermanent-mold-cast cylinder head. In the past, use of aluminum cylinder heads in the automotive industry has been limited by cost. Alcoa has completed bench-mark tests — evaluating several adhesives — which indicate that an adhesive joint will perform well in a properly designed cylinder head.

Many complicated and intricately cored castings — such as timing-gear housings, compartmented oil pans, intake manifolds and fuel-filter bases — could be replaced by die castings or full permanent-mold castings adhesive-bonded to produce the item.

Bearing material can be adhesive-bonded to forged aluminum connecting rods, or to any casting or forging where good bearing characteristics are needed.

Aircraft and Military

Structural adhesives represent the most recent advance in adhesive technology, and their functional properties have been critically tested in applications such as helicopter rotor blades.

These blades are severely stressed structures and offer a challenge in the choice and arrangement of materials that will give maximum life under fatigue types of loading. One helicopter manufacturer has combined aluminum extrusions, clips and skins with a modified phenolic tape to make blades that have lap-shear strengths of 4,200 to 5,000 psi (see Fig. 18). These blades are used in a 44-ft-diameter rotor.

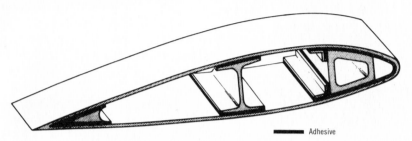

Adhesive

Fig. 18—A helicopter rotor blade in which aluminum extrusions, clips and skins are bonded with a modified phenolic tape. These blades have lap-shear strengths of 4,200 to 5,000 psi; the rotor diameter is 44 ft.

Fig. 19—The Strategic Air Command supersonic B-58 Hustler makes extensive use of structural adhesives of the modified, phenolic and epoxy type in aluminum-foil or glass-fiber honeycomb cores for various components.

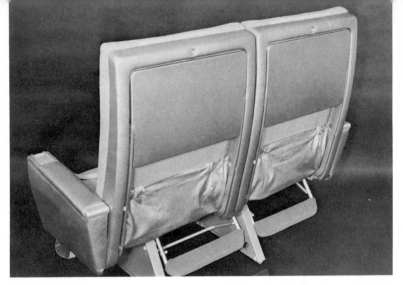

Fig. 20—In these aircraft seats, decorative vinyl fabrics were adhesive-bonded to the aluminum frame.

Structural adhesives of the modified phenolic and epoxy type are also used extensively in aluminum-faced panels with aluminum foil or glass-fiber honeycomb cores, for components, such as control surfaces and trim tabs, etc., in jet aircraft. In fact, the B-58 bomber is made up almost entirely of adhesive-bonded components. The uniform holding power of the adhesive joining the aluminum sheet facings to the core offers many advantages over conventional riveted construction, including exceptional resistance to sonic fatigue.

Structural adhesives are used in extremely low-temperature (cryogenic) applications. Cryogenic fluids (liquefied gases), used in missiles for both fuels and oxidizers, have raised a number of problems associated with the choice of materials. The extensive use of adhesive bonding in the Centaur missile, and the anticipated use of adhesives in future space vehicles, have focused attention on problems related to bonded joints at temperatures as low as -423°F. Table 1 shows average shear strengths of seven different adhesives at various temperatures. These were determined by lap-shear tests on ½-in.-overlap 0.063-in. alclad 2024-T3 aluminum specimens. As the number of cryogenic applications increases, there will be a growing demand for adhesives designed specifically for these extreme temperatures.

RESULTS OF LAP-SHEAR TESTS ON ½-IN.-OVERLAP 0.063-IN. ALCLAD 2024-T3 ALUMINUM SPECIMENS   Table 1

Adhesive Type	Tempera- ture, °F	Average Strength, psi	Type of Failure (Average) Cohesive, %	Adhesive, %	Average Adhesive Thickness, mils
Epoxy-nylon "A"	78	5790+	25	75	2.1
	—100	5470+	. .	. .	2.5
	—320	5050	32	68	3.3
	—423	4580	3	97	4.2
Epoxy-nylon "B"	78	4170	29	71	6.3
	—100	5550+	. .	. .	4.8
	—320	3300	0	100	5.4
	—423	2510	0	100	5.7
Epoxy-nylon "C"	78	6110	83	17	1.0
	—100	5210+	. .	. .	. .
	—320	3790	68	32	2.0
	—423	3370	57	43	2.1
Nitrile-modified phenolic	78	2960	77	23	4.7
	—100	5020	60	40	4.9
	—320	4400	2	98	4.3
	—423	1710	0	100	4.4
Epoxy-polyamide A	78	2180	9	91	1.6
	—100	1850	29	71	1.3
	—320	1760	29	71	1.4
	—423	1640	55	45	3.3
Epoxy-polyamide B	78	2460	65	35	0.3
	—100	2380	25	75	0.4
	—320	1900	50	50	0.4
	—423	2010	15	85	1.0
Polyurethane	78	1310	. .	. .	. .
	—100	3100	. .	. .	. .
	—320	2980	. .	. .	. .
	—423	2710	. .	. .	. .

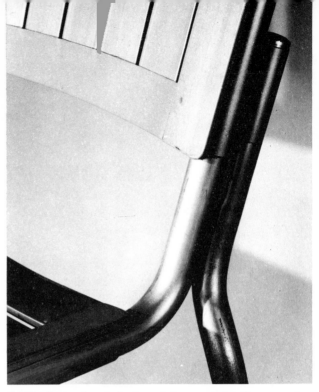

Fig. 21—The bonding of aluminum chair components with an epoxy-type adhesive helps maintain mechanical strength of the aluminum and makes significant reductions in subsequent finishing operations.

Furniture

Complicated chair-base castings are often required for certain modern design configurations. A chair base that is difficult to cast as one piece can be made by joining several simpler castings with adhesives, thus fulfilling the designer's concept and achieving an economical and structurally sound product.

Miscellaneous

The structural joining of two hemispheres with a one-part, heat-cured epoxy adhesive illustrates the use of high-strength aluminum alloys in designing vessels to withstand high internal or external pressures. The sphere shown in Fig. 22 uses ¾-in.-thick aluminum alloy 6061-T6 plate; it is designed to withstand external pressures up to 3,000 psi, and has withstood pressures in excess of 4,000 psi.

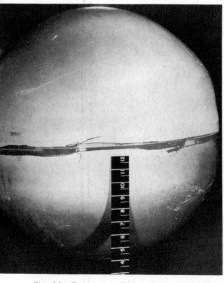

Fig. 22 — To create a 24-in.-diameter aluminum sonar sphere with high resistance to external pressure, two hemispheres were joined using a half-lap joint bonded with a one-component epoxy. The core for the adhesive was combined with the aging of aluminum alloy 6061-T4 to 6061-T6. During pressure testing, the sphere buckled at around 1,000 psi. The adhesive did not fail until the aluminum began to peel away during collapse.

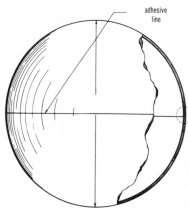

adhesive
line

Fig. 23 — Drawing of the sonar sphere illustrated in Fig. 22, showing the joint design.

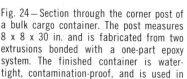

Fig. 24 — Section through the corner post of a bulk cargo container. The post measures 8 x 8 x 30 in. and is fabricated from two extrusions bonded with a one-part epoxy system. The finished container is watertight, contamination-proof, and is used in marine, rail and highway transportation.

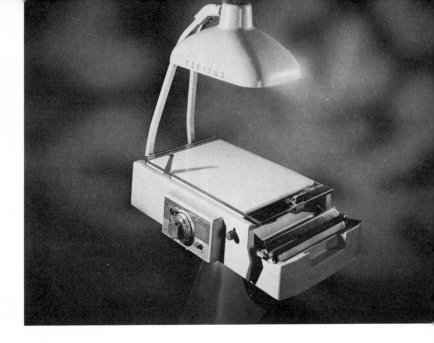

Housings for typewriters, computers, photographic equipment (Fig. 25), etc., can often be adhesive-bonded in many instances where fasteners are usually employed.

Cast heads for fire extinguishers may easily be joined to aluminum sheet bodies.

Decorative vinyl films are laminated to aluminum sheet with adhesives. These products, such as Alcoa Vynalate* Sheet, provide a stiff, lightweight sheet with a decorative plastic facing and can be used for luggage, equipment enclosures, decorative panel facings, etc. Vynalate Sheet is now available with both interior or exterior weathering vinyl film. Tedlar† and other films are laminated to aluminum sheet to serve similar markets — particularly for applications where external weathering is a factor.

Foil-paper laminates find their greatest use in the packaging industry, where printed aluminum foil provides an attractive package that is an effective barrier against moisture, vapor, odor, light and air.

In the packaging field there is a myriad of adhesive applications. Thus, the subject is a study in itself and must be treated in a separate publication.

* Trademark of Aluminum Company of America
† Registered Trademark of E. I. duPont de Nemours & Co., Inc.

Fig. 25—The platen of this Kodak Verifax Copier is made of polyurethane foam adhesive-bonded to an aluminum base. (Courtesy of Eastman Kodak Company)

Fig. 26—The lightweight, forged aluminum handle of this trowel was adhesive-bonded to the steel blade.

Summary

The type of adhesive that will be chosen for any application is generally determined by service requirements and by the equipment and method established for the fabrication of the specific product involved. In many cases, the properties of the adhesives far exceed the requirements. In general, the two basic considerations are: 1) What are the desired properties of the adhesive necessary to do the job? 2) What application method is most suitable?

The fabrication of aluminum products presents many possibilities for the effective use of adhesives, among which the most logical areas are:

—where adhesives are the only possible solution to a fastening problem—either because of the properties of the material to which aluminum will be joined, or because of special properties required of the finished assembly.

—where, even though mechanical fastening or welding are feasible, adhesives may give superior performance.

—where adhesives can produce cost savings in production.

—where adhesives may be used to complement other joining methods.

Chapter 2

SURFACE PREPARATION

THE DEGREE to which aluminum must be pretreated is related to the service application and the ultimate bond strength desired. If optimum strength is not a determinant, an adhesive of lower bond strength may be employed, and simple surface cleaning by vapor degreasing is usually adequate. Where maximum strength, good bond reproducibility and maximum resistance to deterioration are required, a more thorough surface pretreatment is necessary.

Many attempts have been made to explain some fundamental aspects of metal adhesive bonding by describing various adhesion factors. Theory can explain, in general, why these factors are important, but it is another matter to predict the specific properties of untried adhesive-adherend combinations. It is particularly difficult to predict durability — or service life — because the generalized concepts of adhesion theories are likely to apply only to initially obtained adhesion.

The general excellence of aluminum-adhesive bonds, obtained after sulfuric acid-dichromate pretreatment of aluminum, has been widely accepted. This is largely the result of an early aircraft industry program in which Alcoa participated. The excellent resistance to exposure of adhesive bonds made in this manner has been reported by Alcoa researchers and many others. Other aluminum surface treatments have included sandblasting to improve mechanical interlocking, or the preparation of a chemically active surface on aluminum to increase specific adhesion factors.

Since a number of variables affect the problem of surface pretreatment, it is not desirable to set down standardized, oversimplified rules guaranteeing permanently satisfactory aluminum adhesive bonds. The following factors, however, should be considered in the selection of a bonding method:

1. the degree of structural bond strength required;
2. the degree and adherence of surface contamination initially present;
3. the durability of the bond in relation to the type of exposure conditions it will encounter in service;
4. the type of adhesive under consideration. (In most cases, reliable correlations have not been established between the available pretreated surfaces of aluminum and the specific molecular structures of various adhesive classes.)

Solvent Cleaning

Where loosely adhering dirt, grease or oil is present, organic solvent degreasing has been most widely employed. Some methods for simple surface cleaning are:

1. *vapor degreasing with trichloroethylene or perchloroethylene (the solvent should be cleaned or changed on a regular schedule);
2. scrubbing with a highly volatile solvent such as acetone or methylethyl ketone, followed by air drying;
3. *where oil or grease is the only contaminant, it may be possible to clean aluminum for low bond-strength applications by passing the metal through a hot-air oven to burn off organic contamination.

Alcoa has made exhaustive tests on thousands of composite products of adhesive-bonded aluminum to nonmetallics for architectural uses (i.e., curtain-wall panels, siding, roof panels, etc.),

*Cleaning by either of the above methods is commercially available in most Alcoa products and should be ordered as "Free-from-Oil."

under a variety of cycling high- and low-temperature and humidity conditions. These tests indicate no apparent advantage in chemical pretreatment of the aluminum surface, beyond effective solvent or surface cleaning for the applications mentioned.

Chemical Cleaning

In high-strength applications, particularly where aluminum is to be bonded to itself or to other metals, chemical pretreatment is usually mandatory.

Of the many methods that have been employed, the following pretreatments have shown the most evidence of favoring good bond strength, bond reliability and durability. To determine which of these pretreatments is most appropriate for your specific needs, consult your Alcoa representative and your adhesive specialist.

1. Sodium Dichromate-Sulfuric Acid Method
  a. Clean the surface in perchloroethylene or trichloroethylene solvent. (Vapor-degreasing practices are also widely used, and would be preferable for high-speed commercial production.)
  b. Air-dry the surface (the higher metal temperature in a vapor-degreasing operation would cause more rapid drying).
  c. Submerge the cleaned aluminum surface for 10 minutes in a 150°-155°F solution of 10 parts by weight of concentrated sulfuric acid to 1 part of sodium dichromate to 30 parts of distilled water.
  d. Flush the treated surface with fresh water, submerge the part, remove and air-dry at room temperature or, preferably, at temperatures to 150°F.
  e. Solution requires lead-lined tank and adequate exhaust system.

2. Chromic Acid-Sulfuric Acid Method
  a. Clean the surface in perchloroethylene or trichloroethylene. (Vapor-degreasing practices are also widely used, and would be preferable for high-speed commercial production.)
  b. Air-dry the surface (the higher metal temperature in a vapor-degreasing operation permits more rapid drying).
  c. Submerge the cleaned aluminum surface for 5 minutes in a 160°-180°F solution whose proportions are 1 gallon of concentrated sulfuric acid to 45 ounces of chromic acid to 9 gallons of distilled water.

d. Flush the treated surface with fresh water, submerge the part, remove and air-dry at room temperature or, preferably, at temperatures to 150°F.

e. Solution requires lead-lined tank and adequate exhaust system.

3. Alcohol-Phosphoric Acid Method

a. Clean in perchloroethylene or trichloroethylene solvent. (Vapor-degreasing practices are also widely used, and would be preferable for high-speed commercial production.)

b. Air-dry the surface (the higher metal temperature in a vapor-degreasing operation permits more rapid drying).

c. Submerge the degreased or lightly contaminated aluminum surface in the proprietary alcohol-phosphoric acid solution, diluted with water according to the manufacturer's specifications. If ambient-temperature solutions are used, about 10 minutes' soaking is common; about 1 or 2 minutes may suffice where heated solutions are employed.

d. Rinse the surface thoroughly in cold water and follow by drying. In some instances, the manufacturer may recommend an acid rinse before final drying. Drying in an air oven at 120°-150°F is preferable to ambient air drying.

e. Solution requires rubber- or plastic-lined tank or a 300-type stainless steel tank. Special exhaust system is not required when solutions are used at ambient temperatures.

4. Chromate Chemical-Conversion-Coating Method

Cleaning of the aluminum surface may be similar to (a) and (b) of Method No. 1, or an inhibited alkaline cleaner may be used. A number of proprietary inhibited alkaline cleaners are available, and immersion times and solution temperatures must be adjusted according to the manufacturer's recommendation. An inhibited alkaline cleaner may be used as the precleaner for any of the above chemical treatments, as well as for the chromate-conversion coating, but all traces of alkalinity must be rinsed from the surface before further processing (most readily accomplished by using a dilute acid solution).

c. Immerse the aluminum surface in the conversion solution, diluted according to the manufacturer's recommendations. Experience is important in choosing an optimum immersion time, and the manufacturer's recommendations can only be taken as general guides.

d. The surface should be rinsed in a cold-water overflow tank, followed by a hot-water rinse if rapid drying is desired.

e. Solution requires 300-type stainless steel tank and an adequate exhaust system.

5. Paste-Type Cleaners

Some emphasis has been placed on organic paste-type cleaners, which can simultaneously clean and chemically treat an aluminum surface. A unique advantage of these pastes is that they can be readily applied in the field, requiring only adequate water supply for flushing the metal surface. It should be pointed out that the contact time needed to produce an adequate chemically treated surface with these pastes is about 1 hour to 1½ hours at ambient temperature. Some time reduction (to about 30 minutes) can be obtained by controlled heating. Such pastes can be applied over most soil-, ink- or lubricant-contaminated surfaces, but bonding surfaces that are heavily encrusted with salt or other chemicals should first be rinsed thoroughly with water.

6. Anodizing

Although anodizing an aluminum surface would not be the most economical pretreatment for adhesive bonding, this method does offer an excellent surface in many cases. In a comparison of initial bond strength and bond durability on anodized and chemically treated aluminum surfaces, it was noted that surfaces prepared by sulfuric acid-chromic acid pretreatment or proprietary alcohol phosphoric acid cleaners usually show higher initial bond strength and superior exposure performance under moderate hot-wet exposures. Under severe exposure conditions, such as immersion in a 3½ percent salt solution, however, significantly superior bond-strength retention was demonstrated by the anodically treated surface.

Mechanical Surface Preparation

While the best chemical treatments must be highly recommended for preparing aluminum surfaces for general bonding, they may not be necessary under all circumstances. In the case of general bonding with low-strength adhesives, no greater benefits from chemical treatment can be realized beyond those gained by simple solvent cleaning of the surface.

Mechanical methods for preparing surfaces include surface blasting, wire brushing, sandbelt grinding, and rubbing with emery cloth or metal wool. There are instances where mechanical methods are used in conjunction with solvent cleaning or chemical treatments. Where heavy deposits of soil or corrosion products overlay the metal surface, it is often most economical to mechanically roughen the surface.

Grease or oil should be removed with a solvent before the mechanical cleaning operation. Repeat solvent cleaning if there is residual contamination after blasting.

Organic and Inorganic Surface Coatings

Many organic coatings have been actively studied at Alcoa relative to the finishing of aluminum. The most important have been the vinyls, alkyds, vinyl-alkyds and the thermoplastic and thermosetting acrylics. Varying degrees of thermoplasticity or thermoset are required in these coatings. This is a consequence of the wide variability in metal-forming techniques, which are usually performed after the coating has been applied and cured.

The initial adhesive-bond strength between laminated, painted aluminum surfaces cannot be greater than the strength of the bond between the paint film and the aluminum. Good elastomeric-phenolic adhesives can form a bond to aluminum which is about as strong as the best paint-to-aluminum bond. The strength of an epoxy adhesive bond will usually exceed the strength of the paint-to-aluminum bond.

A number of inorganic primers have also been investigated — most of which were specifically designed to give increased protection against environmental corrosion. The subject matter relative to these inhibitive, inorganic coatings (developed for better paint adhesion and corrosion prevention) overlaps that of the chemical-conversion coatings discussed earlier in this chapter.

Chapter 3

ADHESIVE CLASSIFICATIONS

Epoxies

EPOXY ADHESIVES are those most commonly used in joints that require high strength and structural integrity. The user must be aware, however, that there are many available modifications of epoxy adhesives. This abundance of variations results partly from the wide range of problems a designer encounters in adapting adhesive bonding to actual applications. Many adhesive manufacturers formulate "custom-made" adhesives to fit a particular application.

Epoxy adhesives are thermosetting: They undergo a chemical change when cured, and there is no means by which they can be returned to their original state. Curing is accomplished by the addition of hardeners to the basic resin. The hardener (or activator) present in one-component systems is activated by exposure to elevated temperatures—usually from 250° to 500°F—for a specified period of time. In epoxy adhesives where curing is accomplished at room temperature, the hardener component is added just prior to application. It should be mentioned, however, that some multiple-component epoxy adhesives require elevated-temperature curing.

In order to examine the various attributes of epoxy adhesives, they will be classified for subsequent discussion as follows:

1. **One-component**
   a. High-strength — flexible
   b. High-strength — semirigid, better elevated-temperature service and chemical resistance
2. **Multiple-component**

1. One-component

a. High-strength — flexible — A compromise has existed in epoxy adhesives with respect to strength and flexibility. That is, those adhesives which exhibited high strength when subjected to shear or tensile stresses were rather poor in peel or cleavage, because of the rigidity of the cured product. Additional modification to gain more flexibility usually resulted in a decrease of tensile or shear properties.

Several innovations have made it possible to obtain even higher strengths than those previously available with epoxy adhesives, while providing relatively high flexibility and peel or cleavage resistance. One of these was accomplished through nylon modification. Use of nylon-modified epoxies is often limited, since they are normally in film form and are relatively expensive.

Another innovation concerns a special process of polymerization. While this epoxy system is about as strong as nylon-modified systems, it is only half as flexible.

These two types of epoxy formulations may be used in applications where both high strength and flexibility are required. They do not retain their properties much above 200°F, which limits their use in elevated-temperature service. These adhesives are serviceable down to -67°F, however, and some of the nylon-epoxy films can be used in cryogenic applications with fairly good strength maintained to -400°F.

Most of the adhesives in this class are cured about one hour at 350°F, with contact pressure to obtain optimum properties. Much shorter curing times at 400°F will still provide properties higher than other epoxy adhesives; and Alcoa has actively engaged in a number of development programs in this area.

Typical applications for this class of epoxies are pressure vessels, architectural structural components, structural joints in the transportation field and aircraft honeycomb panels.

b. High-strength — semirigid — Applications for early epoxy formulations were limited because of poor peel or cleavage strength. Despite the fact that stronger and more flexible epoxy adhesives are available today, there is still need for these rigid adhesives because of their good elevated-temperature properties.

For most of these materials, there is a wide latitude in curing cycles from a few hours at 300°F to a few minutes at 500°F. Most of the formulations are in paste form, but some are available in solid rod, powder or film. The powder adhesives can be applied by immersing the heated part into the powder or into a fluidized bed consisting of air-suspended powder. The rod is applied to a heated part in a manner similar to that employed in soldering. Again, the powder or rod can be melted at a temperature below that which would thermoset the material. The prepared parts are then coated by dipping them into the molten adhesive.

Most of these adhesives are serviceable from -30° to 400°F or above. Epoxies modified with a phenolic resin have been used in cryogenic applications down to -400°F. It should be reiterated that most epoxy adhesives require only contact pressure in curing. One exception to the rule is the family of phenolic-modified epoxy adhesives: These require pressure during the curing cycle. In severe exposures, such as boiling-water immersion or halogenated hydrocarbon propellants, epoxy adhesives of the semirigid type are the only materials known to be durable. The durability is of course relative — some percentage of strength is lost — but most other adhesives would fail completely in these types of exposures.

Typical applications for these epoxy materials may be found in joining refrigerator or evaporator tubing, automotive engine components and aircraft honeycomb. One of the adhesives used in the B-58 Hustler is a phenolic-modified epoxy film.

2. Multiple-component

Essentially, most multiple-component systems sold as packaged adhesives contain two parts: the epoxy resin with fillers and/or modifiers already added, and the activator or hardener. Most of these adhesives can be cured at room temperature and will take from a few hours to as many as 48 hours.

Like the one-component epoxies, two-part formulations are available in various combinations of flexibility and strength. This is normally a matter of compromise; the stronger the adhesive in shear, the less flexible it is likely to be.

Generally, these materials are in liquid or paste form. The parts must be proportioned accurately and mixed thoroughly just prior to their use. Most of these formulations have a pot life of one-half hour to two hours, after which they will be too rigid to make application possible. The activator, which represents the force for cross-linking the resin polymers, must be added in the prescribed amount for all possible reactions to occur, and no excess of activator should remain in the mixture. For the same reasons, the combined material must be adequately mixed to make sure all reaction does take place.

For high rates of production, equipment is available to store the two parts separately; mixing and proportioning of components are accomplished in the head of a pressure gun. In some of the available two-component epoxies, flexibility is controlled by adding varying amounts of the hardener. It is obvious that in these instances the mixing ratio is less critical, since there are several ratios available.

Two-component adhesives that cure under ambient conditions are employed in applications where heat curing is either impossible or uneconomical. Heat-curing epoxies should be used whenever possible, because as a rule the strength is higher, and there are several other advantages. (These will be discussed later.) The performance of two-part epoxies can be improved by heating in the 150° to 250°F range; but if higher temperatures — above 250°F — are permissible, one-component epoxies might as well be employed.

Generally, the chemical, elevated-temperature and water resistance of two-component formulations are not as good as those of one-part epoxies. It is presumed that this may be caused to some extent by the sensivitity of these materials to surface preparation, particularly when they are cured at room temperature.

This matter of surface preparation is basic, and the user of adhesives should be aware of the limitations of epoxies. In many instances, heat-curing adhesives have been employed with only solvent cleaning or vapor degreasing as a surface preparation. Adequate adhesion to the surface is possible because of the increased wetting ability of these materials under the stimulus of heat. Room-temperature-curing epoxies, however, normally require chemical cleaning to obtain adequate adhesion. It may not be just a matter of reduced shear strength. When bonding on a production scale and employing a room-temperature-curing epoxy adhesive with solvent cleaning, more bond variability may occur. Therefore, it has been the practice to suggest chemical cleaning when using two-part epoxies for curing at room temperature.

COMPARISON OF PROPERTIES FOR EPOXY ADHESIVES[1]   Table 2

Type	Tensile-Shear Strength[2] psi	T-peel[3] Strength, lb/in.
1. One-Component (Heat-Cured)		
a. High-Strength Flexible	4,000-7,000	12-160
b. High-Strength Semirigid	4,500-5,500	2-6
2. Two-Component (Room-Temperature-Cured)	1,000-4,000	2-30

[1] All test specimens were chemically cleaned—chromic acid-sulfuric acid solution.
[2] Tensile-shear strength—Alclad 2024-T3—½-in. lap.
[3] T-peel strength, 9 mil—5052-H18 alloy.

Modified Phenolic Adhesives

Historically, phenolic-based adhesives were the first synthetic resins employed in structural adhesives. During World War II, a considerable amount of this material was used in aircraft honeycomb production.

Phenolic resins are generally modified with thermoplastic resins such as nylon or vinyl compounds. Phenolics can also be modified with elastomers, such as nitrile rubber. As with epoxy adhesives, modification is required to provide flexibility in the joint. However, the higher flexibility is accompanied by lower shear strength.

The method of nomenclature whereby the major adhesive constituent is placed first in the name description is certainly more practical and more exact, but it is not always followed in practice. In this publication we shall use this method—placing the major adhesive constituent first in any name description.

The nitrile-modified phenolic adhesives have had their chief application in the bonding of brake-shoe linings and aircraft honeycomb. The modified phenolics most frequently used with aluminum have been the stronger but less flexible nylon- or vinyl-modified adhesives. These have been used for structural laminations, as exemplified by aircraft honeycomb or snow skis.

Unlike most epoxies, these phenolic-based adhesives are often supplied in solvent. It is therefore necessary to dry the applied adhesive thoroughly before assembling the parts for curing. Drying can be accomplished at room temperature or at temperatures below 200°F.

Phenolic adhesives require high unit pressure during curing. The following is a typical curing schedule for a modified phenolic adhesive:

1. Predry for one hour prior to assembly.
2. After assembly, preheat for 15 minutes at 325°F under contact pressure.
3. Apply 250 psi pressure for 15 minutes at 325°F.
4. Cool under pressure.

Phenolic adhesives often require two or more coats to build up sufficient film thickness, with drying periods between the successive coats.

Phenolic-based adhesives are available as liquid, film or supported film. The liquid form can be brushed, sprayed, roller-coated or flow-coated. The films are often used with a light primer coat — usually less than 1 mil of the same composition in liquid form. Some film is supported with an open-weave cloth, often glass-fiber mesh.

Phenolic-based adhesives are generally good in most common types of chemical exposures. The thermoplastic-modified phenolics are generally higher strength than those modified with an elastometer.

Typical properties which may be expected for thermoplastic- or elastomer-modified phenolic adhesives are 2,000-5,000 psi in shear, and 5-20 lb per in. width in T-peel.

Elastomeric-Based Adhesives
Natural-Rubber Adhesives — Natural rubber, one of the earliest raw materials employed in formulating adhesives was, from the outset, considered as a possible bonding material because of its initial tack, tack retention and outstanding flexibility.

The long tack-retention properties of natural rubber have made it ideal for pressure-sensitive adhesive applications. Adhesives based on natural rubber usually set by evaporation of the material used for dispersing the rubber—commonly organic solvent or water. Chemical catalysts or accelerators may be used at ambient temperature, or heat curing can be employed to improve strength and heat resistance. This rubber is then said to be vulcanized. The relative strength of vulcanized rubber is still low in comparison to the thermosetting adhesives, and natural-rubber-based adhesives are unsuitable for many applications. In practice, natural rubber would rarely be employed alone, but would be modified with a variety of synthetic resins to improve tack, increase the cohesive strength, elevate the heat resistance, and generally improve the adhesion to many surfaces.

Natural-rubber adhesives find their widest application in bonding nonmetallic materials such as leather, fabrics, paper and rubber products. They may, however, also be used for attaching these nonmetallics to aluminum surfaces. The elasticity of the natural-rubber bond is advantageous where the metal surface is relatively unyielding to dimensional change in humidity, or where it moves more than the nonmetallic material under the stimulus of heat.

Methods of bonding with natural-rubber adhesives are, for the most part, similar to the procedures for the entire class of elastomers. They are generally available in organic solvent or water solutions of wide viscosity range. These may be sprayed, roll-coated, curtain-coated, brushed, knifed or trowled on one or both surfaces.

When making the bond at ambient temperature, it is often most convenient—and most conducive to bond reliability—to apply the adhesive to both surfaces, let the solvents evaporate until the surfaces are tacky, and then press them together—minimum pressures suffice to make the bond. If the adhesive is applied to only one surface, higher pressures are usually necessary to make satisfactory bonds. This increased pressure may be particularly effective when one surface is relatively porous and fingers of adhesive are literally forced into its surface pores. Higher strength and heat resistance can be achieved either by accelerating the adhesive-curing reaction with a chemical additive or by applying external heat. External heating must always be accompanied by the simultaneous application of pressure, so that the surfaces are held in intimate contact while the adhesive is achieving maximum strength. The choice can also be made as to whether heating is to be performed before the adhesive has lost all of its surface tack (some solvent remains in the adhesive) or after it has achieved a tack-free state (all solvent has been removed).

Resins of different softening points may be added to natural rubbers to achieve varying degrees of tackiness and ultimate strength. The recommendations of adhesive suppliers will vary accordingly as to drying time for optimum tack or temperature for maximum bond strength. An important advantage of these adhesives is that they manifest high initial tack and immediate bond strength; hence, they are generally classified as contact-type adhesives. In water-latex dispersions of natural rubber, some compatibility problems with aluminum may exist.

Natural rubber has good resistance to deterioration by water, but poor resistance to oils, organic solvents and chemical oxidizing agents. The natural-rubber molecule crystallizes (stiffens) at about -30°F, and water-latex, natural-rubber emulsions must be protected from freezing, which can readily damage their adhesive properties.

Chlorinated Natural-Rubber Adhesives—This modified natural rubber resulted from early attempts to produce resins from natural rubber. It is made by chlorinating a rubber solution in a solvent such as carbon tetrachloride.

As a resin, the outstanding property of chlorinated rubber is its resistance to acids and alkalies. As a base for adhesives, its use lies mainly in bonding natural and synthetic rubbers to metals. Such adhesives have actually been used to prime metal surfaces prior to bonding with neoprene- or nitrile-based adhesives.

One procedure for bonding a rubber product to aluminum is to apply a chlorinated-rubber adhesive to the metal surface—to evaporate the solvent to obtain a tacky surface—and then to press the rubber product section on this surface. The assembly may finally be heat-cured to produce the ultimate bond.

Chlorinated rubber itself has good resistance to water, some oils, salt spray and bacterial growths, and similar behavior is found in chlorinated-rubber adhesives. Resistance to organic solvents in general is poor, and the practical temperature service limit is around 280°F.

Cyclicized- or Isomerized-Rubber Adhesives—Cyclicized rubber is produced commercially by treating natural rubber with acids or metal salts. An increase in density occurs, which is explained by a 65 per cent conversion of the linear polymer to a cyclic polymer.

Hard resins made from cyclicized rubber have been successfully used in lining tanks, since they possess good adhesion to metals. Solutions of cyclized rubber are used, therefore, to prime metal surfaces prior to bonding with other rubber-based adhesives. Adhesives formulated with cyclized rubber form a tough bond to metal surfaces.

The adhesive is applied to both surfaces to be bonded, and is dried to a nontack condition. The surfaces are joined and held in intimate contact while the assembly is heated to achieve vulcanization of the rubber interface.

Adhesives containing cyclized rubber have good resistance to water and bacterial contamination, but are generally poor in the presence of oils and aromatic and chlorinated solvents. The maximum service temperature is about 140°F.

Rubber-Hydrochloride Adhesives — When natural rubber is dissolved in an aromatic or chlorinated solvent, and hydrogen chloride is passed through the solution, rubber hydrochloride is formed. This material has been used principally in the form of thin, transparent film for general utility in the packaging industry. Some combinations have been made into adhesives, because of their inherent property of good adhesion to metal surfaces. The hydrochloride-containing adhesive acts as a primer for bonding a variety of rubbers to metal.

The methods of using cyclized-rubber adhesives and hydrochloride-containing adhesives are similar. Application of adhesive to both surfaces is followed by drying to a nontack condition and then by heat-vulcanizing the adhesive interface.

Good resistance to water is common to all the natural-rubber variations listed. Rubber hydrochloride is essentially insoluble in ethers, alcohols and esters, but is soluble in aromatic hydrocarbons and chlorinated hydrocarbons. Its maximum service temperature is about 230°F.

GR-S (SBR) Rubber Adhesives — GR-S rubber, a copolymer of butadiene and styrene, is the largest volume synthetic rubber manufactured in the United States today. In general, any of the synthetic rubbers have better resistance to sunlight, chemicals and oils than natural rubber.

GR-S rubber adhesives are usually inferior to natural rubber in initial tack, tack retention and flexibility. Because of the particularly low tack of GR-S rubber, adhesives containing it are often compounded with tackifiers and plasticizing oils. It is possible to obtain a variety of desired properties (increased strength, heat resistance, heat flexibility) by blending this synthetic rubber with other rubbers or with various resins. If a lower-cost adhesive is desired, the use of certain fillers or extenders is recommended. GR-S rubber adhesives are available in both organic-solvent solution and water-latex emulsion form. The solvent most commonly used is naphtha, which means that the adhesive can be employed with surfaces — such as plastics — that would be deleteriously affected by aromatic or ketonic solvents.

The largest proportion of GR-S rubber production has been used for products other than adhesives, because the bond strength of such adhesives is similar to that of the cheaper, reclaimed rubber-base adhesives. The use of GR-S rubber for metal bonding is therefore limited, and most general lists of the best materials for bonding with GR-S adhesives do not include aluminum. GR-S adhesives, however, have been investigated by Alcoa for bonding aluminum to porous nonmetallic surfaces, when products lower in cost than neoprene or nitrile adhesives are desired. Both sheet- and foil-gauge aluminum have been bonded. In industry, GR-S adhesives are ordinarily used for bonding plastics, rubber, sponge, wood, fabrics, and floor and wall coverings.

The usual method of bonding is to apply the adhesive, in thin syrup or heavy mastic consistency, as uniformly as is economically feasible (spray, roller-coat, curtain-coat, brush or mechanical spreader).

It is desirable in bonding at ambient temperature to apply the adhesive to both surfaces and to combine them while some tack is still present. Pressure from contact to 100 psi may be employed (depending on the type of material to be bonded); 20 to 50 psi is probably a good average in production. There is no necessity for any dwell time under pressure, although the initial bond strength (about 75 per cent of final strength) will continue to increase over a seven-day period after bonding. It may sometimes be more expedient in production to combine the drying phase with a heat-activation process, so that the degree of tackiness in the adhesive is caused more by the heat than by the residual solvent in the surface layers of the adhesive. Momentary pressure, such as that produced by passing through a rotary press, can produce a satisfactory bond. Finally, it is possible to regenerate a tack condition in a dried GR-S adhesive film by heating the surface to about 180°F in a hot-air oven or under infrared lamps.

The GR-S adhesives have shown tendencies to crystallize with aging as a result of oxidation. This may limit the use of this particular adhesive in some applications. Further studies are necessary to evaluate the magnitude of this change and the degree to which it may affect ultimate service life.

Neoprene-(Polychloroprene) Rubber Adhesives — Neoprene rubber is very closely related chemically to natural rubber. Its enhanced strength, higher temperature resistance and better aging properties as compared with natural rubber are highly significant. Neoprene is the type of synthetic rubber most widely employed today in adhesives used to bond aluminum. It is usually dispersed in aromatic hydrocarbons and ketones, but it is also available in water-base latex form. These water-dispersed latex neoprenes may also be combined with the protein casein to produce a class of adhesives that is extensively employed in bonding wood. The nonflammable and nontoxic nature of these adhesives can also be important in some applications.

The range of neoprene applications covers the bonding of a great number of porous or nonporous, metallic or nonmetallic surfaces. Neoprene adhesives are particularly useful in fabricating high-volume composites of aluminum to nonmetallic plastic insulating materials, or of aluminum to wood products for architectural applications. High-speed production methods may be employed, since these adhesives have immediate green strength, and no dwell time at elevated temperature is necessary to secure an adequate and durable bond. Varying degrees of strength and flexibility are available in neoprene adhesives. Accommodation can thus be obtained in the bond between aluminum and nonmetallic laminated structures whose component parts may have different coefficients of heat expansion, or undergo dimensional change under varying humidity.

Neoprene adhesives are generally suitable for applications involving continuous exposure at temperatures up to 200°F, and they can withstand short exposures to considerably higher temperatures. The combination of flexibility, good heat resistance and durability makes neoprene adhesives ideal for bonding aluminum-faced sandwich panels in curtain walls and residential building construction. The neoprenes are versatile enough to find general application in bonding plastics, leather, rubbers, fabrics and plywood to aluminum. Neoprene adhesives may also bond to aluminum a wide variety of nonmetallic insulation and commercial building materials such as hardboard, cement-asbestos board, gypsum board, glass-fiber-reinforced polyester and vegetable-fiber boards.

Most of the neoprene adhesives set by a solvent-release mechanism (organic solvent or water). Four different procedures have been employed in bonding aluminum with neoprene adhesives:

1. The adhesive is applied (by spray, roller-coater, curtain-coater, brush or mechanical spreader) to one or both surfaces, and allowed to air-dry until tacky. The surfaces to be joined are pressed together (preferably in a rotary or platen press). Considerable immediate green strength is present, and the bond will develop about 85 percent of final strength within a few hours. Within a period of about 24 hours, sufficient strength is developed for most applications.

2. After applying the adhesive as above, the surfaces are heated by hot-air convection or infrared until the solvent is volatilized out of the adhesive. The surfaces are then combined immediately and pressed firmly together in a rotary or platen press. If the other surface to be bonded to the aluminum in an unsymmetrical laminate is nonmetallic, its different coefficient of thermal expansion may present a problem in trying to secure a flat laminate. It may be necessary to provide some cooling while maintaining flatness by pressing. The lower the temperature of satisfactory bonding, the better the opportunity to secure a flat final laminate.

3. After applying the adhesive, the surfaces are heated or allowed to air-dry until a no-tack surface is obtained. In this condition, many neoprene-adhesive-coated surfaces can be stacked and stored for periods ranging from a few days to a few weeks and held for subsequent reactivation. When the final aluminum laminate is to be made, the surface is mist-sprayed with an appropriate organic solvent, and the adhesive develops a tacky surface condition. Pressure applied in the usual fashion should then furnish a satisfactory bond. More reliable bonds may be made by adhesive-coating both surfaces, although it is necessary to restore tack to only one surface.

4. The same steps are employed to arrive at a tack-free condition, as in Procedure 3, but after tack is restored by heating the surfaces, they are combined in a rotary or platen press. Higher reactivating temperatures are necessary for some neoprene adhesives that contain other resins blended in to secure maximum service temperatures. The high combining temperatures used may produce bowed laminates on cooling; this problem must be anticipated.

Neoprene adhesives have good resistance to water, some oils, aliphatic hydrocarbons, weak acids and alkalies and bacterial contamination. They are generally unsuitable in contact with aromatic hydrocarbons, ketonic solvents and strong oxidizing agents. Neoprene adhesives have adequate room-temperature shear strengths (200-800 psi) for many applications involving the joining of aluminum to nonmetallic materials, but they are unsuited for many metal-to-metal applications where the adhesive might creep under certain conditions of loading and temperature.

A large number of neoprene adhesives have been exhaustively tested by Alcoa for use in bonding aluminum to itself and to nonmetallic materials. These tests cover bond durability and adhesive compatibility with aluminum, under conditions of cycling temperatures from -30°F to 170°F, and water exposures from 100 percent humidity at 125°F to immersion at 165°F. The tensile and stress-rupture values for many neoprene adhesives have also been determined at ambient temperature and at 180°F. These test results are considered necessary for predicting the performance of neoprene adhesives in outdoor applications.

Nitrile-Rubber Adhesives — Synthetic nitrile rubber (buna-N) is a combination of 1, 3-butadiene and acrylonitrile. This rubber has appeared under the names: "Butaprene*," "Chemigum†," and "Hycar‡." All these may be considered synonymous. Nitrile rubber is used extensively for adhesive formulation in aluminum bonding and may be second only to neoprene in popularity. This rubber is, however, employed more extensively than neoprene as a modifier for phenolic resins in formulating phenolic-nitrile adhesives that are generally employed in the structural bonding of metals. A degree of confusion in nomenclature exists in these latter high-strength adhesives, because there appears to be little tendency in the adhesives industry to distinguish them in generic terms from the lower-strength nitrile-phenolic adhesives.

Nitrile-rubber adhesives will bond well to a wide variety of surfaces such as plastics, wood, rubber, paper products, fabrics, glass and metals. This adhesive is preferred for bonding a plastic like polyvinyl chloride to aluminum because the plasticizer will generally not soften the adhesive if plasticizer migration occurs. Alcoa has been particularly interested in the use of nitrile-rubber adhesives for bonding aluminum to itself or to other materials in cases where the structure will be exposed to continuous high humidity or direct contact with liquid water. The overall cohesive strength of the nitrile adhesive is maintained in water exposures, as

* Trademark of Firestone Tire & Rubber Co.
† Trademark of Goodyear Tire & Rubber Co., Inc.
‡ Trademark of B. F. Goodrich Chemical Co.

well as its strength of adhesion to an aluminum surface. The greater range of adhesive properties available in neoprene types has meant that neoprenes continue to have the widest application for general bonding.

One of the outstanding advantages of nitrile rubber itself is its excellent resistance to oils; hence aluminum structures in contact with oils are often bonded with nitrile-rubber adhesives. The compatibility of water-dispersed, rubber-latex adhesives with aluminum is often open to question in high-humidity environments, because of the alkaline nature of the latex. A nitrile-rubber, water-latex adhesive is available that is compatible with aluminum even when exposed to continuous humidity. This adhesive, referred to as a carboxylated nitrile, may be of particular interest where the bonded material to aluminum is sensitive to organic solvents and a cold bonding process is dictated.

Nitrile-rubber adhesives have good resistance to oils, water and bacterial growth. Their resistance to many solvents, such as the aliphatic hydrocarbons, is good, as it is to most acids (except for the strong oxidizing ones). The maximum service temperature (about 250°-300°F) is somewhat higher than for neoprene adhesives. Nitrile-rubber adhesives, while superior to neoprene-rubber adhesives, are still unsuitable for certain structural applications under some conditions of loading and temperature. The maximum shear strengths of nitrile-rubber adhesives range up to 1,000 psi when they are ambient-temperature-bonded, and they may extend to 2,500 psi when bonded with heat and pressure. This is higher than the maximum for many neoprene-rubber adhesives. The water resistance of most nitrile-rubber adhesives is excellent and certainly satisfactory for most lower-strength outdoor weather applications, such as panels for curtain-wall construction. Representative nitrile-rubber adhesives from most manufacturers have been subjected by Alcoa to accelerated testing for bonding aluminum to itself and to a wide variety of nonmetallic materials.

Butyl-Rubber Adhesives — Butyl rubbers are copolymers of a diene such as butadiene and an olefin such as isobutylene. They have not been used to any extent in adhesives because of poor strength characteristics and an excessive tendency to creep even under low loads. Butyl rubbers do have certain properties, such as exceptionally low permeability to gases and good resistance to water and chemicals, which favor their use in sealing compounds. Butyl-rubber formulations for this purpose have been used in aluminum curtain walls, with good sealing properties and good compatibility with aluminum construction surfaces.

Polysulfide-Rubber Adhesives – Polysulfide rubbers are prepared from sodium tetrasulfide, chlorine and waste olefin gases. They vary from a viscous liquid to a tough, rubber consistency, depending mainly on the relative amount of polysulfide present in the reaction. The polysulfide rubbers have several characteristic deficiencies that make them unacceptable as major raw materials for adhesives. Nonetheless, their relatively low strength, tendency to creep under low loads, and low resistance to elevated temperatures are not necessarily handicaps for application as sealants. Other properties, such as good resistance to water, solvents and oils, and retention of flexibility at temperatures down to -80°F, are further important advantages for sealants. Some polysulfide rubbers are, however, employed to reduce the rigidity of two-part thermosetting epoxies. These modified adhesives have been employed with aluminum and are compatible under accelerated test conditions, although they do not maintain initial bond strength as well as many unmodified epoxy adhesives. The polysulfide sealing compounds have excellent records for durability and adhesion to aluminum surfaces. The major products of most manufacturers have been thoroughly tested by Alcoa.

Silicone-Rubber Adhesives – Silicone rubbers are prepared by the reaction of silicon tetrachloride and a Grignard reagent to form an organo-silicon-chloride polymer.

Silicone adhesives may be employed on pressure-sensitive tapes. The same adhesive formulations as those on the tapes can also be used to bond aluminum to glass, paper, some plastics and silicone rubber itself. The excellent dielectric properties of silicone adhesives have prompted their use on insulating electrical tapes. Some silicone-rubber adhesives are in the form of a paste, and are used primarily for bonding cured silicone rubber to aluminum, other metals and various inorganic surfaces. In all instances, the good peel strength of silicone adhesives is a property not present in many of the other adhesives.

Silicone adhesives that are sold in solutions go through the usual tack states when the solvent is almost dissipated. In the case of adhesives compounded for use on pressure-sensitive tapes, the tack remains in the surface until it is contaminated or bonded to another surface. The paste-consistency silicone adhesives may be of room-temperature or heat-curing variety. In most instances, only contact pressure is required while the cure is being effected.

The silicones in general are noted for their exceptionally good resistance to high temperatures. Silicones by themselves will withstand continuous temperatures from about -130°F to 480°F. They have excellent water resistance and are also resistant to dilute acids and alkalies; and they also have excellent aging properties. Of particular pertinence to their use in some adhesives is their retention of flexibility at low temperatures.

A considerable volume of silicone is also employed to make a variety of one-part adhesive-sealer caulking materials. These thixotropic paste-like materials are usually extruded from cartridge containers by pressure as a bead, and cured by contact with the moisture present in the air to a tough but flexible consistency with excellent resistance to a wide range of temperatures.

Reclaimed-Rubber Adhesives—The rubber used in compounding reclaimed-rubber adhesives is obtained by processing vulcanized-rubber, natural-rubber and synthetic-rubber scrap. Much reclaimed rubber is derived from used tire stock and, as such, contains considerable cotton, sulfur and other filler material. It is important to note, however, that reclaimed rubber is carefully processed to meet the specification requirements of the Rubber Reclaimers Association. Reclaimed rubber has relatively low tensile strength, low elongation and low resistance to abrasion. Mixtures of reclaimed stock and natural or synthetic rubbers are often used in adhesives to augment the poor properties of reclaims, when production costs must be kept down.

Selection of a reclaimed-rubber adhesive for an application is usually motivated by economy, since the properties of reclaimed adhesives offer no specific advantages in other areas. Reclaimed-rubber adhesives do, however, offer a good compromise of properties; they are usually modified with resins, tackifiers and fillers, giving some range in consistency, strength and elevated-temperature resistance. Reclaimed-rubber adhesives are often used as substitutes for neoprene- or nitrile-rubber adhesives. This occurs where an organic-solvent-type adhesive is preferred, but some material is present that would be deleteriously affected by the aromatic or ketonic solvent necessary for disbursing the neoprenes and nitriles. In such cases, the lower price of the reclaimed-rubber adhesives may be a bonus. In many applications (for example, aluminum architectural structures), the use of a reclaimed rubber may be rejected because the adhesive must resist lengthy weathering exposure. Reclaimed rubbers, however, should definitely be considered for many indoor low-bond-strength aluminum applications, especially when making laminations of low-cohesive-strength fiberboards to aluminum. Reclaimed-rubber adhesives are unsuitable for structural applications for two reasons: their tendency to creep even under light loads; and their low maximum service temperature of 160°F.

The reclaimed rubbers are usually bonded by drying out the solvent until a tacky condition results; a bond is then made by pressing the two surfaces together. Reclaimed-rubber adhesives may also be bonded hot, after accelerating the removal of solvent with hot-air or infrared heating. Heat- or solvent-reactivation methods are usually not employed with reclaimed-rubber adhesives.

The best reclaimed-rubber adhesives are good enough in resistance to water to pass a 100 per cent humidity test at 125°F. Test procedures involving temperatures higher than 160°F may cause failure of reclaimed-rubber adhesive bonds; but if these test temperatures are significantly above the practical field-exposure limits, reclaimed-rubber adhesives may still be adequate. In Alcoa's evaluations, reclaimed rubbers have been shown to be most satisfactory for bonding aluminum to porous nonmetallic structures for interior service.

Thermoplastic-Resin Adhesives

The thermoplastic resins are employed in compounding many industrial adhesives. They have excellent properties of adhesion to aluminum and most metals, and thus are widely employed in metal adhesive formulations. Since these resins are heat-fusible, they are not usually employed in an unmodified state for structural bonding of metals. Combinations of thermoplastic and thermosetting resins are employed for structural bonding; for a discussion of such adhesives, please refer to other sections on structural bonding.

Polyvinyl-Acetate Adhesives — The basic linear polymer may be prepared by reacting acetic acid with acetylene to form vinyl-acetate monomer, and then polymerizing to get a polymeric resin. Vinyl-acetate adhesives are available as milky-appearing, nonflammable water emulsions and as colorless organic-solvent solutions. The emulsions are more widely used in industry, but many of them must be evaluated for possible incompatibility with aluminum in high-humidity exposures.

The vinyl-acetate adhesives are popular in the wood industry (particularly furniture) because they are easy to apply, have high initial tack and are relatively quick-setting. Shoe manufacturing, bookbinding and packaging also use these adhesives in volume. Aluminum foil, plastic films and paper laminates have all been combined with vinyl-acetate adhesives. If proper care is taken to remove all water from the vinyl-acetate emulsions in the drying of the adhesive film, then compatibility with aluminum may be expected.

Most vinyl-acetate adhesives set by water loss. As the last traces of water disappear, the surface becomes tacky; pressure should then be exerted to achieve bonding. The presence of some green strength at this time means that effective bonding of materials such as foil, paper and leather can be achieved with the momentary contact afforded by a nip roll. Clamping may be necessary where more rigid materials such as wood or sheet metal are to be joined. A clamped joint is usually strong enough to handle in about 30 minutes. Bonds may be obtained by application of adhesive to one or both surfaces, depending on the method of lamination and the materials to be bonded. Adhesive application to both surfaces is preferred when a nip-roll operation is desired, to achieve the speed necessary for high production. If the materials to be combined are under such tension that adhesive application on one surface will not generate sufficient green strength to maintain an intimate bond after passing through the nip roll, then two-surface coating *must* be employed. For applications where clamping is practical and one or more surfaces are porous, a high-viscosity version of the vinyl-acetate adhesive can minimize the risk of producing an adhesive-starved joint when adhesive is applied to only one surface. When bonding two nonporous surfaces, the solvent is completely removed and bonds are obtained by heat sealing or by organic-solvent reactivation of the dried films.

Maximum service temperatures of about 120°F (unless greatly modified with higher-temperature resins) restrict the use of these adhesives in many exterior applications exposed to sunlight. Creep occurs in these adhesives at low loads, thus making them unsuited for structural applications. Vinyl-acetate adhesives have only moderate resistance to water and poor resistance to organic solvents. They do, however, have good resistance to oils and to bacterial contamination.

Polyvinyl-Chloride Adhesives — Polyvinyl chloride is generally produced by the action of chloride or hydrochloric acid on ethylene or acetylene, respectively. In most adhesive applications, polyvinyl chloride is copolymerized with polyvinyl acetate for further compounding into adhesives. The main application of polyvinyl chloride-polyvinyl acetate adhesives is in bonding vinyl plastics to metal or glass. In some instances, polyvinyl chloride has been copolymerized with neoprene or nitrile rubbers for bonding the same surfaces. If water solutions are employed and long-time service is desired, the compatibility of the adhesive should be checked against an aluminum surface in the presence of humidity.

Acrylic Adhesives — The best-known thermoplastic resins of this type are the acrylates and methacrylates. They are formed by hydrolyzing and esterifying acrylonitrile or acetone cyanohydrin, respectively. Properties vary with molecular weight — the resins becoming tougher as the molecular weight increases. Because there are highly polar substituent groups in the polymer chain, the resins have excellent adhesive qualities.

Acrylic adhesives have been used for bonding plastics, glass, leather, cloth and metals. Bond strengths vary, depending on the kind of acrylate employed, as well as on the method of application. Adhesives of this type are to be recommended mainly for bonding aluminum to nonmetallic porous materials, where there is need for only medium resistance to water. In order to obtain sufficient bond strength for structural applications, these adhesives must usually be heat-cured; such applications would still be limited by the low maximum-service temperature.

Acrylic adhesives are available as solutions, as emulsions, or as polymer-monomer mixtures, which may be cured by ultraviolet, heat or chemical catalysts. Bonding from a solution consists of the usual procedure — drying to the point of tackiness and then joining two tacky surfaces. If one or both surfaces are porous, it is possible to join the surfaces by clamping or pressing while the solvent dissipates through the material. Some acrylics may be applied as a solution, but the solvent is then removed by thorough drying. The tack-free surface is then held under pressure against a second surface, and the bond is made by application of external heat.

The maximum service temperature of the simplest acrylic adhesive is about 125°F, but blends containing higher homologous acrylics can significantly raise this service temperature. The acrylics have medium water resistance, good resistance to oil and thermal shock, but poor organic-solvent resistance.

The acrylics have been used as modifiers for several types of thermosetting resins with gratifying results. The most common types have been epoxy acrylics and phenolic acrylics, which have a high water resistance when used to laminate wood to plastics or plastics to metals.

Hot-Melt Adhesives — Hot-melt adhesives fall into the classification of thermoplastic-resin adhesives in behavior; i.e., solid at room temperature, liquid and workable when heated. They are particularly adaptable to high-speed assembly operations because they set up and reach their maximum strength as soon as they cool. Other advantages are their indefinite shelf life, reusability and freedom from waste. They are offered in a wide range of polymers, with softening points from 100° to 500°F.

The polyamides are one family of resins that can be varied to give hot melts of almost any desired temperature — over a span of several hundred degrees. These materials are compatible with aluminum. They are most commonly employed, however, as modifiers for both structural and nonstructural adhesives to improve flexibility and resistance to impact.

Hot-melt adhesives are employed widely in the packaging field, sometimes to bond various materials to aluminum foil. Hot melts are also employed as side-seam cements in fabricating metal, paper and combination metal-and-paper containers.

Another large class of hot-melt materials, the microcrystalline waxes, is useful for making temporary bonds to nonporous materials such as metals and glasses. They have good resistance to water and bacterial growth, but low solvent resistance.

A summary of the adhesive properties discussed in this chapter is given in Table 3, page 61.

SUMMARY OF RELATIVE PROPERTIES OF ADHESIVE CLASSIFICATIONS

Table 3

Adhesive Classification	Shear Strength	Peel Strength	Flexibility	General Chemical Characteristics						High-Temperature Resistance	Low-Temperature Resistance	Creep at Elevated Temperature	Reference Page
				Water	Oil	Salt Spray	Fuels	Solvents	Outdoor Resistance				
Epoxy (High-Strength, Flexible)	A	A-B	C	B	A	B	A	A	B	C	A	A	
Epoxy (High-Strength, Semirigid)	A	D	D	A	A	A	A	A	A	A	A-B	A	
Epoxy (Multiple-Component)	B	C-D	D	C	A	C	B	A	B-C	C	B	A	
Phenolic (Thermoplastic-Modified)	A	B-C	C	A	A	A	A	A	A	B	A	A	
Phenolic (Elastomeric-Modified)	B	B	B	B	A	B	B	B	B	A	B	B	
Natural Rubber	D	C	A	B	D	C	D	D	B	C	B	D	
Chlorinated Rubber	D	C	B	B	C	C	C	D	C	B	B	C	
Cyclicized Rubber	D	C	B	B	D	C	D	D	C	D	C	D	
Rubber Hydrochloride	D	C	A	B	C	C	C	C	C	C	C	C	
GR-S (SBR) Rubber	D	C	B	B	D	C	D	D	B	C	C	C	
Neoprene Rubber	C	B	B	A	B	B	B	B	B	C	B	C	
Nitrile Rubber	C	B	B	A	A	B	A	B	A	B	B	C	
Butyl Rubber	D	C	B	B	D	C	D	B	B	D	C	D	
Polysulfide Rubber	D	C	B	A	B	B	A	B	A	D	B	D	
Silicone Rubber	C	A	A	A	C	A	C	C	A	A	A	C	
Reclaimed Rubber	C	C	B	B	D	C	D	C	C	C	C		
Polyvinyl Acetate	B	C	C	C	B	C	D	D	D	C	C	C	
Polyvinyl Chloride	C	B	B	C	C	C	C	C	C	D	C	D	
Acrylic	C	C	C	C	B	C	C	D	C	C	B	C	
Hot Melt	C-D	B-D	B-D	B-C	C-D	D	D	C-D	B-D	A-D	C-D	B-D	

Note: A = Very good B = Good C = Fair D = Poor

Chapter 4

THE DESIGN
OF AN ADHESIVE-BONDED JOINT

PROPER ENGINEERING design of joints is directed toward the main objectives of obtaining maximum strength for effective use and of making it possible for manufacturing departments to produce the given job satisfactorily. In adhesive bonding, perhaps even more than in other modes of joining, joint design is a vital factor influencing the strength properties of an entire product, assembly or structure.

The selection of a joint design may be strongly influenced by the appearance desired in the finished part. Similarly, joint design may be subject to limitations in production facilities (heat, pressure and adhesive application techniques), or to allowable production costs, or to special problems of ultimate service conditions, or to other general considerations.

Since these influences are extremely variable, their relation to projects involving joint design must be left to the individual designer. On the other hand, experience in the design of joints of adhesive bonding has revealed some factors that should be useful in other applications.

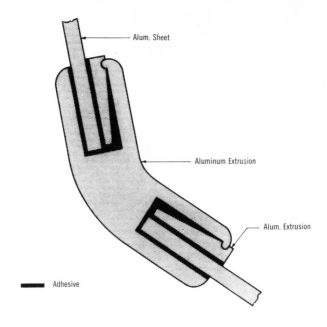

Fig. 27—A cross section of the joint configuration for a seaworthy wedge-type joint designed for adhesive bonding.

Selection of Adhesives and Adherends

Certain considerations in this connection have already been explained and compared (see especially Adhesive Classifications, Table 2, page 45). A point to be emphasized here is the necessity for giving consideration to the material (or materials) to be bonded before an adhesive is selected.

When designing joints to bond dissimilar materials, selection of adhesives must take into consideration the varying bonding abilities that may exist with permeable and impermeable adherends. In the same way—since it is desirable to minimize stresses arising from differences in coefficients of thermal expansion—the design of a joint to bond dissimilar materials may be based on the use of an ambient-temperature adhesive, or it may be based on a larger-than-usual factor of safety. In any event, the preliminary selection of an appropriate adhesive will be an important factor.

In structural or stressed assemblies, the adhesive joint should have a strength equal to, or stronger than, the adherends.

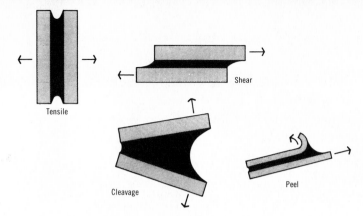

Fig. 28—The effect of various kinds of stresses on an adhesive-bonded joint.

General Features of Joint Design

Whatever the configuration ultimately adopted for a particular joint, the basic design intentions will be (1) to stress the adhesive in its strongest direction; (2) to keep the bond continuous; and (3) to have a maximum of bonded area as an important part of the total assembly strength.

With high-strength bonds, it is generally desirable to keep the adhesive layer as uniform in thickness as possible, inasmuch as variations may cause concentrated stress points in the joint.

The actual thickness of adhesive is also a critical general factor in joints of various types. As a general rule, the adhesive layer should be sufficient to avoid a "starved" joint and accompanying poor bond, and yet should be thin enough to obtain good tensile and shear strength. It may be said that the thinner the adhesive layer, the stronger the joint within the limits of avoiding a "starved" joint. Stronger joints are also associated with the uniformity of the adhesive layer and with the parallelism of the adhered surfaces.

It has been theorized that with high-strength adhesives, the smoother the bonding surfaces, the stronger the joint will be.

General Design Considerations

Most of the adhesives used for bonding aluminum to itself and other materials are at their best strength when loaded in shear or tension, and are weakest in cleavage or peel (Fig. 28). In usual practice, joint design is directed to place the adhesive in shear,

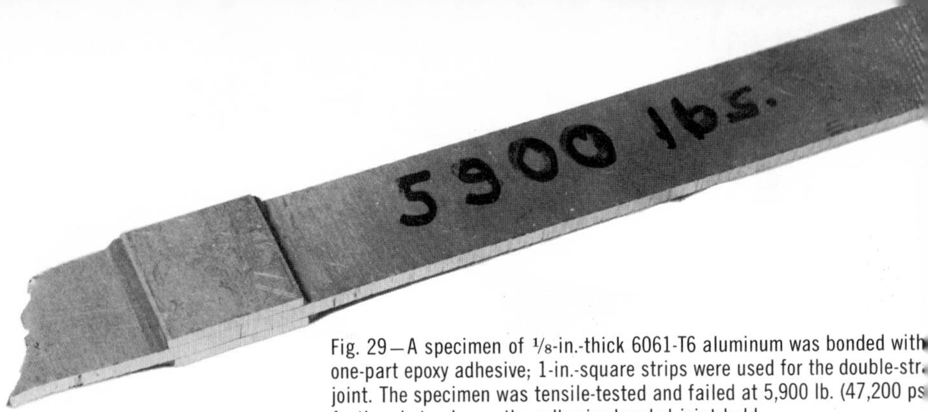

Fig. 29—A specimen of ⅛-in.-thick 6061-T6 aluminum was bonded with one-part epoxy adhesive; 1-in.-square strips were used for the double-str joint. The specimen was tensile-tested and failed at 5,900 lb. (47,200 ps As the photo shows, the adhesive-bonded joint held.

while peel and cleavage stresses are prevented or held to a minimum. Such shear-loaded joints are more easily fabricated than tensile-stressed joints, and are therefore more often used. Some of the detailed considerations for the geometry of joints may be indicated by a brief examination of some typical examples (Fig. 30). The basic and familiar shear-loaded joint is the lap, commonly used in joining relatively thin sheets. In a single-lap joint under stress, there is a tendency for the joint bond area to distort because of the eccentricity of the applied load. This applies peel stress to the adhesive at the edges of the lap, the bond may tend to peel or cleave apart (see Fig. 31).

Under low loads, the simple lap described may be adequate. For higher loads, however, the design may have to be strengthened by using metal of greater thickness and/or yield strength, or by increasing the width and/or depth of the joint lap. Moreover, there is an important difference in the joint-strengthening effect between widening and deepening the overlap. For a given depth of lap and thickness of metal, the strength of a lap-shear joint is directly proportional to the *width* of the lap; thus, a 2-in.-wide joint will be twice as strong as a 1-in.-wide joint. It should be noted that this linear relationship does not hold constant for an increase in the *depth* of the overlap. The edges of the lap carry a larger proportion of the load than does the interior area of the bond; consequently, the unit strength gained per unit increase in depth of overlap gradually becomes lower. After a given depth of lap is reached, there is no longer a proportionate increase in the strength of the joint.

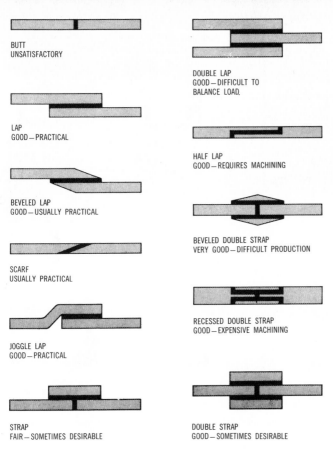

BUTT
UNSATISFACTORY

LAP
GOOD—PRACTICAL

BEVELED LAP
GOOD—USUALLY PRACTICAL

SCARF
USUALLY PRACTICAL

JOGGLE LAP
GOOD—PRACTICAL

STRAP
FAIR—SOMETIMES DESIRABLE

DOUBLE LAP
GOOD—DIFFICULT TO
BALANCE LOAD.

HALF LAP
GOOD—REQUIRES MACHINING

BEVELED DOUBLE STRAP
VERY GOOD—DIFFICULT PRODUCTION

RECESSED DOUBLE STRAP
GOOD—EXPENSIVE MACHINING

DOUBLE STRAP
GOOD—SOMETIMES DESIRABLE

Fig. 30—The relative practicality of a variety of joint designs.

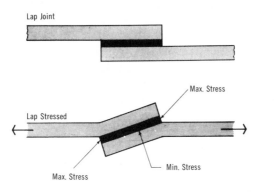

Lap Joint

Lap Stressed

Max. Stress

Min. Stress

Max. Stress

Fig. 31—Schematic drawing of a lap joint showing areas of minimum and maximum stress when the joint is in tension.

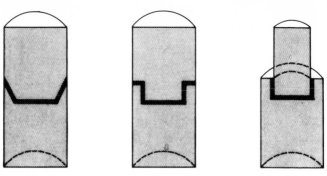

Fig. 32—Three joint designs for adhesive bonding of round bars.

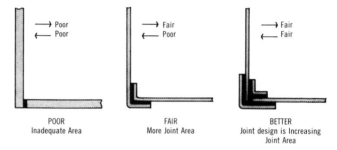

POOR
Inadequate Area

FAIR
More Joint Area

BETTER
Joint design is Increasing
Joint Area

Fig. 33—Cleavage stress areas in angular or corner joints; the relative strengths of three such designs are shown here.

Very often, the best approach to strengthening a high-load lap joint is to use a more efficient configuration. Fig. 30 shows some variations in the design of joints for flat plates or sheets. The scarf joint and beveled lap are more efficient than the simple lap, since they provide axial loading and a more uniform stress distribution over the joint bond area. In design for thin metal, however, these more efficient joints may present problems in manufacture; the joggle lap or a strap joint may then be the best choice.

The ordinary butt joining of, say, solid rods is usually not a dependable design in practice. This results from the fact that the stresses during use will only rarely be pure compression, tension or torsion—all well anticipated in the butt—but that they will also include cleavage forces. It is therefore better design to vary from the plain butt by use of recessed tongue-and-groove, scarfed and other configurations (see Fig. 32).

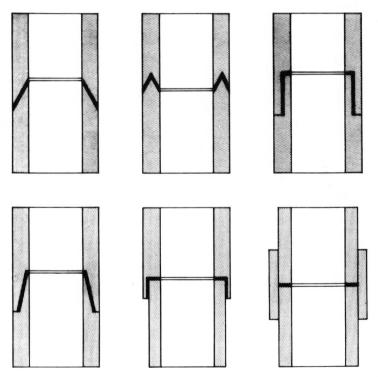

Fig. 34—A few joint configurations that are useful in adhesive-bonding cylinders or tubes.

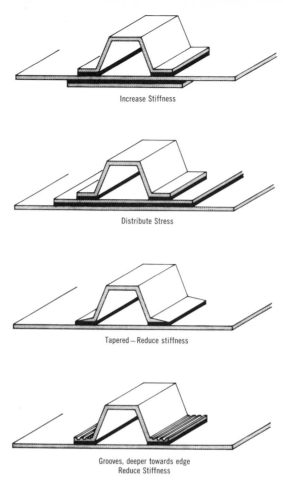

Increase Stiffness

Distribute Stress

Tapered—Reduce stiffness

Grooves, deeper towards edge
Reduce Stiffness

Fig. 35—Some methods of aluminum sheet stiffening that can be obtained by adhesive-bonding extruded aluminum shapes to sheet to reduce peel stresses.

Cleavage stresses (or peel force, depending on the gauge of material used) also arise in angular joints such as corners. These are demanding joints for the designer, and it is often very difficult to achieve more than a compromise reinforcement (see Fig. 33) with given gauges of sheet and usually-specified adhesives.

Cylindrical and tubular joints can be strengthened considerably by proper design. This often requires machining to assure adequate contact area for the adhesive bonding (see Fig. 34).

Fig. 36—An aluminum panel stiffened with aluminum extrusions. The bond was made with a one-part epoxy system. The bending moments on this panel can permit the permanent deformation of the aluminum before the adhesive fails.

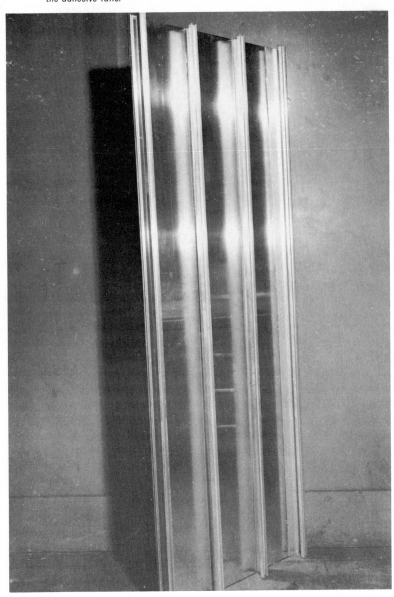

Chapter 5

FACTORS THAT GOVERN
THE SELECTION OF AN ADHESIVE

CHOOSING THE RIGHT adhesive is neither a matter of luck nor simply a question of following a few basic rules. It is a complex problem that requires careful and extensive analysis of many factors, including: the characteristics of the materials to be bonded; environmental and stress conditions under which the joint will function; the available manufacturing or assembly facilities; and, of course, the end use of the bonded component.

In referring to the following list for a given situation, it will, of course, be apparent that certain questions do not apply or are seemingly unimportant. While it is true that some items can be disregarded, it is suggested that consideration be given to as many of the listed factors as possible. This will enable your Alcoa representative and your adhesive specialist to help you make the most appropriate type of adhesive-bonded joint.

1. **The physical characteristics of the materials involved.**
   a) Describe each of the materials that are to be joined.
   b) State all pertinent dimensions of the assembly.
   c) State the known effects of elevated temperatures on the material(s).

2. **The joint configuration if predetermined.**
   Provide an accurate detail drawing.

3. **The loading requirements.**
   State the critical loads (in precise or qualitative terms) under the following:
   a) tension
   b) shear
   c) peel
   d) cleavage
   e) fatigue
   f) impact

4. **The service-temperature limits.**
   State the maximum and minimum temperatures that may be anticipated.

5. **The joint environment.**
   State the expected environmental conditions in terms of the following:
   a) water
   b) humidity
   c) solvents
   d) chemical or petroleum products
   e) bacteria or fungi, etc.

6. **The shop facilities.**
   Provide information on the available facilities for the following operations:
   a) oven curing
   b) hot-press curing
   c) roller press
   d) adhesive application
   e) surface preparation

7. The production rate.
Evaluate and estimate production rates that are economical, efficient and provide the necessary time for producing a well-made joint.

8. The reason for using an ahesive-bonded joint.
Make a comparison with other appropriate joining methods in terms of the following:
a) economy
b) functional or aesthetic (finishing requirements)
c) fabricating speed

Chapter 6

SAFETY PRECAUTIONS

THOSE WHO PERFORM adhesive-bonding operations are more likely to encounter health problems associated with environment than problems relating to safety practices. Environmental health problems are ordinarily associated with the materials used for surface preparation of the metal, with the adhesive materials themselves, or both.

Surface Preparation

Solvent Cleaning — Proper precautions must be taken during vapor degreasing with trichloroethylene or perchloroethylene. Although less toxic than carbon tetrachloride, these solvents will produce narcosis if vapors are present in high concentrations; therefore, vapor concentrations must be kept within safe limits. Vapor-degreasing operations must be done in well-ventilated areas, and the practices recommended by equipment and solvent manufacturers should be followed.

When using trichloroethylene, it is necessary to use a stabilized solvent and to make certain that it is cleaned regularly in order to prevent the reaction of the solvent with aluminum.

Highly volatile solvents, such as acetone and methylethyl ketone, can create fire and health hazards. Exhaust ventilation is necessary to control vapor concentrations, except in certain cases where the cleaning operation is small and infrequently performed.

Organic solvents will remove the protective oils of the skin, and unless the skin is protected from solvent contact, dermatitis problems can result.

Chemical Cleaning — The most serious problems associated with chemical cleaning result from skin or eye contact with highly corrosive materials.

Chemical reaction will not be vigorous because of the low temperatures of the cleaning solutions; therefore, misting and its concomitant inhalation hazard is not likely to be a major problem. (Mist rising from the cleaning solvents is, however, highly irritating to the respiratory tract.)

Skin contact with cleaning solvents should be kept to a minimum, and any material that touches the skin should be promptly removed by washing. Extreme care must be taken when handling chromates, since repeated contact will cause dermatitis. In some cases, the person affected becomes sensitized to such an extent that any subsequent contact, even with minute quantities of chromate, will cause a flare-up. Gloves and eye protection are essential at all times when handling chemical solutions.

Mechanical Surface Preparation — In most cases, mechanical surface preparation will merely create nuisance problems that result from the generated dust. Such problems can be eliminated simply by using proper ventilation or respiratory protective devices.

On the other hand, surface-blasting techniques may require specific controls.

In the surface-blasting process, the size of the work, the duration of the operation and the composition of the abrasive determine the precautionary measures. Such measures can become quite elaborate; i.e., booths and supplied air respirators.

Organic and Inorganic Surface Coatings — Health problems associated with the use of surface coatings are almost exclusively attributable to the solvent vehicles, and a wide range of solvents may be involved. Coatings should always be applied in well-ventilated work areas. The type of solvent and the size of the operation determine if general ventilation is sufficient or if additional exhaust ventilation is necessary. Spray painting usually requires exhaust ventilation. Brief or temporary spraying operations may necessitate a respirator as protection against mists and solvent vapors.

Application of Adhesives

There are few health hazards ordinarily associated with fully cured adhesive materials; however, some of the monomers are potentially toxic. Health problems arising from the application of adhesives to aluminum are overwhelmingly due to nonpolymeric components (solvents, catalysts, plasticizers, fillers, etc.) and not to the basic polymers.

The vast majority of adhesive components are contained in organic solvent solutions or dispersions, although in some cases water dispersions are used. The most common types of organic solvents encountered are petroleum derivatives, aromatics, ketones, alchohols and chlorinated hydrocarbons. Most of these solvents and their solvent vapors are flammable, and users must be made aware of their potential fire and explosion hazards. Because solvents are toxic, it is important that the mixing of adhesive components and the application of adhesive to aluminum be done in well-ventilated areas; exhaust ventilation is required in most cases. Continuous skin contact with solvents, or uncured resin dispersions and solutions, must be avoided. Gloves and safety glasses are an absolute necessity.

Contact dermatitis is frequently associated with epoxy components; occasionally associated with polyester-resin components; but only rarely associated with polyurethane-resin components. Good habits of personal cleanliness help minimize dermatitis problems. **Never use solvents to clean the skin!**

There are specific hazards to which users should be alerted. Although many of the uncured epoxy resins can be handled without ill effect (especially those of higher molecular weight), almost all of the amine hardeners used with them are irritants as well as sensitizers. In some cases, the amine vapors have caused asthmatic symptoms.

Special care should be taken to avoid skin contact with methyl-methacrylate monomer. This resin has been known to cause skin sensitization.

Where fiberglass is used as a filler material, the minute spicules can, by mechanical action alone, cause a dermititis. The particles embed themselves in the skin causing irritation, itching, scratching and, frequently, secondary infection. Protective clothing should be used when handling this material.

Catalysts used for polyesters are usually organic peroxides, and such compounds are capable of exploding spontaneously as well as from shock, friction or heat. They are often mixed with other materials to minimize this hazard. One must be aware of this hazard in order to take appropriate precautions during storage and handling.

Because virtually all adhesive components are combustible, hazards are almost inevitable when such materials burn. Decomposition under the influence of heat produces a myriad of breakdown products, and these vary as the composition of the burned material varies. Heat, lack of oxygen, and the presence of carbon monoxide are the overriding toxic factors.

Chapter 7

GLOSSARY

A

Acetone — a colorless, volatile liquid ketone, used as a solvent for many organic compounds.

Acidulated — characterized by a very low acidity.

Acrylic — any one of a group of thermoplastic resins made by polymerizing esters of acrylic acid or methacrylic acid.

Activator — a substance or mixture of substances added to an adhesive for the purpose of promoting the curing reaction.

Adherend — a body which is held or joined to another body by an adhesive.

Adhesion — the adhering or sticking together of substances in contact with each other.

Adhesive compatibility — the ability of an adhesive and joined material to maintain bond quality that causes no significant deterioration of either.

Aging properties — the chemical and physical properties of an adhesive after exposures to a given environment over a period of time.

Aliphatic hydrocarbons — compounds containing only hydrogen and carbon, having an open chain structure.

Alkaline cleaner — a cleaning preparation that provides the characteristic properties of a caustic-like material (usually inhibited).

Alkyd — any one of a group of thermoplastic synthetic resins prepared by the reaction of certain alcohols with certain acids, and generally used as a surface coating.

Ambient temperature — the temperature of the surrounding air.

Anodizing — a controlled, electrolytic process whereby a protective oxide film is built up on a metal anode surface.

Aromatic Solvents — Solvents which are chemically related to benzene — a colorless, liquid hydrocarbon.

B

Binder — that component of an adhesive formulation which creates an internal adhesive function rather than a surface adhesive function.

Block, blocking — an unwanted adhesion between touching layers of a material, occurring under moderate pressure during storage or use.

Butadiene — a hydrocarbon that is derived either from ethyl alcohol or petroleum; a vital building block in the formulation of certain important synthetic rubbers.

Butyl rubber — one of the synthetic rubbers; it is produced by the copolymerization of isobutylene and butadiene or isoprene.

C

Carboxylated nitrile — a class of nitrile-rubber, water-latex adhesives.

Catalyst — a nonreacting substance which accelerates the curing of an adhesive when added to the primary reactants.

Cleavage — See Fig. 28, page 65.

Cohesive strength — the degree to which particles within a single adhesive will adhere to one another.

Cold-bond process (or cold pressing) — a bonding operation characterized by the use of pressure without added heat.

Contact pressure — the pressure necessary to merely touch or bring together two surfaces.

Conversion coating — a chemical treatment which displaces or removes the normal oxide coating on a metal with a surface that will be more receptive to bonding. These coatings are usually proprietary products containing a phosphate or chromate compound.

Copolymer — the product formed when two or more monomers are polymerized.

Coring — a body of sand, metal, etc., designed to form interior voids, holes or openings in a casting.

Creep — the dimensional change (after a given time) of an adhesive under load. At room temperature, creep is sometimes called cold-flow.

Cross-linking — the chemical interaction, during curing, of the resin polymers.

Cryogenics — a science of the behavior of substances at extremely low temperatures.

Curing — the process in which the physical and chemical properties of an adhesive are changed by means of a chemical reaction; this is ordinarily achieved by the action of heat and a catalyst.

Curtain-coated: a method of applying liquid adhesives, whereby the adhesive (either in organic-solvent or water solution) is passed through an orifice to direct a curtain or screen onto the surface.

Cyclicized-rubber adhesive (cyclised — Great Britain) — an adhesive formulated with rubber that is produced commercially by treating natural rubber with strong acids or metal salts. Cyclicized rubber is used in adhesives for the purpose of bonding rubber to itself, to metals and to other materials.

Cyclic polymer — a resin in which density has been increased and other properties altered by the conversion of the molecular arrangement from linear to circular patterns.

D

Dwell time — the length of time that bonded surfaces are to be subjected to such factors as heat, pressure, etc.

E

Elastomer — an elastic, rubber-like substance (such as natural or synthetic rubber) which, when stretched beyond its original length, will tend to return to its original length upon release of the stress.

Elastomeric adhesives – natural or synthetic rubber-based formulations.

Epoxy adhesive – an adhesive formulated with a thermosetting resin, formed by the chemical reaction between epichlorohydrin and diphenols.

Esterifying (or esterification) – the process of forming an ester by the reaction between alcohol and an acid.

F

Filler – a material such as aluminum powder, clay or calcium carbonate used to extend an adhesive.

Filleting – used to describe the triangular-shaped adhesive configuration at the junction of a joint.

Fluidized bed – a solid material suspension which may be used to coat surfaces.

G

Galvanic corrosion – a type of corrosion that can occur when dissimilar metals are in contact in the presence of an electrolyte.

Green strength – initial bond strength.

GR-S (SBR) rubber adhesives – adhesives formulated with GR-S rubber, which is a copolymer of butadiene and styrene.

H

Heat vulcanizing – the application of heat to furnish a rubber adhesive with certain qualities (strength, elasticity, resistance to solvents, etc.).

Hydrolyzing (or hydrolysis) – a type of chemical reaction in which water is one of the reactants.

I

Initial bond strength – the amount of unit load (applied on first surface contact) needed to break the adhesive assembly.

Initial tack – the degree of stickiness of an adhesive.

Isomerized-rubber adhesives – adhesive substances having the same elementary composition (i.e., their molecules contain the same numbers and kinds of atoms), but differing in structure, and hence in properties.

K

Ketonic solvents — a class of organic chemical compounds commonly used as solvents.

L

Laminate — a structure made by bonding material in layers.

M

Mastic viscosity — a paste-like consistency.

Methylethyl ketone — a colorless ketonic solvent.

Modifier — an ingredient added to an adhesive formulation to alter its properties.

Monomer — a relatively low-molecular-weight compound, which can react to form a polymer.

N

Neoprene rubber — a synthetic rubber widely used in adhesives.

Nip roll — a roller (or rotary press) through which laminate components are passed to achieve a bond.

Nitrile rubber — a synthetic rubber widely used, both as a major and a modifying ingredient, in adhesives.

O

Olefin — a member of a class of hydrocarbons characterized by marked chemical reactivity.

Organic solvent — an organic solution which dissolves another compound or mixture.

P

Peel stress — See Fig. 28, page 65.

Perchloroethylene — an organic solvent used to preclean adherend surfaces.

Permeability — the ability to pass or penetrate a substance (i.e., penetrability).

Phenolic-based adhesives — adhesives formulated with phenolic resins (i.e., a class of thermosetting resins formed from phenols and aldehydes) and suitable modifiers.

Plasticity — a relative property of adhesives which allows deformation without rupture when force is applied.

Plasticizer — a material incorporated in an adhesive that increases its flexibility, workability or softness.

Plasticizer migration – the movement or diffusion of the plasticizer from a bonded surface into the adhesive film.

Polyesters – a broad classification of synthetic resins.

Polymerization – a chemical reaction in which simple components are linked together to form larger molecules of higher molecular weight.

Polysulfide rubbers – a class of synthetic rubbers of relatively low strength; used primarily in sealants or as modifying agents in adhesives.

Pot life (or working life) – the period of time during which an adhesive (after mixing with accelerator, catalyst, etc.) will remain suitable for use.

Pressure-sensitive adhesive – a type of adhesive that will adhere to a surface at room temperature merely by a briefly applied pressure.

R

Reclaimed-rubber adhesives – the rubber used in compounding these adhesives is obtained by processing vulcanized-natural- and synthetic-rubber scrap.

Residual solvent – solvent remaining in an adhesive after the drying process (evaporation) has taken place.

Resin – any of a class of solid or liquid organic substances of natural or synthetic origin, generally of high molecular weight with no definite melting point.

Roller coating – a method of applying liquid adhesives on a given surface by transferring the adhesive from a cylindrical surface.

S

Shear strength – See Fig. 28, page 65.

Shelf life (or storage life) – the period of time during which a packaged adhesive can be stored under specified temperature or other conditions and still remain suitable for use.

Silicones – organic silicon-oxide polymers.

Strap joint – See Fig. 30, page 67.

Styrene – an unsaturated hydrocarbon which is polymerized with butadiene to make GR-S type synthetic rubbers.

Substrate – adherends.

Supported-film adhesive – a type of material wherein the adhesive film is supported (or backed) by an open-weave cloth (e.g., glass-fiber mesh), which is not removed when making the bond.

Synthetic rubber—commercially produced rubberlike substances. They generally have better resistance to oils, solvents, heat, acids, etc., than natural rubber.

T

Tackifiers—agents used for making an adhesive more sticky.

Tensile strength—See Fig. 28, page 65.

Thermoplasticity—the ability of a substance to be repeatedly softened (by heat) and hardened (by cooling).

Thermosetting—having the property of undergoing a chemical change when cured, by which a substance (previously plastic) becomes difficult to melt (infusible).

Trichloroethylene—an organic solvent often used to clean surfaces.

V

Vapor degreasing—a cleaning method in which articles are suspended above a boiling solvent.

Vinyl—any one of a family of thermoplastic resins, based on the unsaturated vinyl hydrocarbon chemical group.

Viscosity—that property of fluids which can be briefly described as resistance to flow.

W

Wettability—the degree to which an applied fluid can spread on a given solid surface.

One of Alcoa's adhesive bonding laboratories

Chapter 8

TABLES

RESULTS OF LAP-SHEAR TESTS ON ½-IN.-OVERLAP 0.063-IN. ALCLAD 2024-T3 ALUMINUM SPECIMENS — Table 1

Adhesive Type	Temperature, °F	Average Strength, psi	Type of Failure (Average) Cohesive, %	Type of Failure (Average) Adhesive, %	Average Adhesive Thickness, mils
Epoxy-nylon "A"	78	5790+	25	75	2.1
	−100	5470+	..	..	2.5
	−320	5050	32	68	3.3
	−423	4580	3	97	4.2
Epoxy-nylon "B"	78	4170	29	71	6.3
	−100	5550+	..	..	4.8
	−320	3300	0	100	5.4
	−423	2510	0	100	5.7
Epoxy-nylon "C"	78	6110	83	17	1.0
	−100	5210+	..	..	
	−320	3790	68	32	2.0
	−423	3370	57	43	2.1
Nitrile-modified phenolic	78	2960	77	23	4.7
	−100	5020	60	40	4.9
	−320	4400	2	98	4.3
	−423	1710	0	100	4.4
Epoxy-polyamide A	78	2180	9	91	1.6
	−100	1850	29	71	1.3
	−320	1760	29	71	1.4
	−423	1640	55	45	3.3
Epoxy-polyamide B	78	2460	65	35	0.3
	−100	2380	25	75	0.4
	−320	1900	50	50	0.4
	−423	2010	15	85	1.0
Polyurethane	78	1310	..	..	..
	−100	3100	..	..	..
	−320	2980	..	..	..
	−423	2710	..	..	..

COMPARISON OF PROPERTIES FOR EPOXY ADHESIVES[1] — Table 2

Type	Tensile-Shear Strength[2] psi	T-peel[3] Strength, lb/in.
1. One-Component (Heat-Cured)		
a. High-Strength Flexible	4,000-7,000	12-160
b. High-Strength Semirigid	4,500-5,500	2-6
2. Two-Component (Room-Temperature-Cured)	1,000-4,000	2-30

[1] All test specimens were chemically cleaned—chromic acid-sulfuric acid solution.
[2] Tensile-shear strength—Alclad 2024-T3—½-in. lap.
[3] T-peel strength, 9 mil—5052-H18 alloy.

SUMMARY OF RELATIVE PROPERTIES OF ADHESIVE CLASSIFICATIONS

Table 3

Adhesive Classification	Shear Strength	Peel Strength	Flexibility	General Chemical Characteristics					Outdoor Resistance	High-Temperature Resistance	Low-Temperature Resistance	Creep at Elevated Temperature	Reference Page
				Water	Oil	Salt Spray	Fuels	Solvents					
Epoxy (High-Strength, Flexible)	A	A-B	C	B	A	B	A	A	B	C	A	A	
Epoxy (High-Strength, Semirigid)	A	D	D	A	A	A	A	A	A	A	A-B	A	
Epoxy (Multiple-Component)	B	C-D	D	C	A	C	B	A	B-C	C	B	A	
Phenolic (Thermoplastic-Modified)	A	B-C	C	A	A	A	A	A	A	B	A	A	
Phenolic (Elastomeric-Modified)	B	B	B	B	A	B	B	B	B	A	B	B	
Natural Rubber	D	C	A	B	D	C	D	D	C	C	B	D	
Chlorinated Rubber	D	C	B	B	C	C	C	D	C	B	B	C	
Cyclicized Rubber	D	C	B	B	D	C	D	D	C	D	C	D	
Rubber Hydrochloride	D	C	A	B	C	C	C	C	C	C	C	C	
GR-S (SBR) Rubber	D	C	B	B	D	C	D	D	B	C	C	C	
Neoprene Rubber	C	B	B	A	B	B	B	B	A	C	B	C	
Nitrile Rubber	C	B	B	A	A	B	A	B	A	B	B	C	
Butyl Rubber	D	C	B	B	D	C	D	B	B	D	C	D	
Polysulfide Rubber	D	C	B	A	B	B	A	B	A	D	B	D	
Silicone Rubber	C	A	A	A	C	A	C	C	A	A	A	C	
Reclaimed Rubber	C	C	B	B	D	C	D	D	C	C	C	C	
Polyvinyl Acetate	B	C	C	C	B	C	D	C	D	C	C		
Polyvinyl Chloride	C	B	B	C	C	C	C	C	C	D	C	D	
Acrylic	C	C	C	C	B	D	C	D	C	C	B	C	
Hot Melt	C-D	B-D	B-D	B-C	C-D	D	D	C-D	B-D	A-D	C-D	B-D	

Note: A = Very good   B = Good   C = Fair   D = Poor

TYPICAL PHYSICAL PROPERTIES/Wrought Products

Table 4

Alloy and Temper	Density at 20°C[3]		Melting Range, approximate °F	Electrical Conductivity at 20°C (68°F), Percent of International Annealed Copper Standard	Thermal Conductivity at 25°C (77°F), CGS units [1]
	g/cm³	lb/cu in.			
EC-O EC-H19	2.703	0.0977	1195-1215	63 62.5	0.57 0.56
2EC-T6, -T62 2EC-T61 2EC-T64	2.694	0.0973	1150-1210	57 59 60.5	0.52 0.53 0.54
1060-O 1060-H18	2.703	0.0977	1195-1215	62 61	0.56 0.55
1100-O, -H18	2.712	0.0980	1190-1215	59[2]	0.53[2]
1145-O, -H19	2.706	0.0978	1195-1215	61[2]	0.55[2]
1170-O, -H19	2.702	0.0976	1200-1220	62.5[2]	0.56
1180-O, -H19	2.700	0.0975	1210-1220	63.0[2]	0.57
1188-O, -H19	2.700	0.0975	1215-1220	63.5[2]	0.57
1199-O, -H19	2.699	0.0975	1220	64.0[2]	0.57
1345-O, -H18	2.705	0.0977	1195-1215	61[1]	0.55[2]
2011-T3 2011-T8	2.833	0.1023	995-1190	39 45	0.36 0.41
2014-O 2014-T3, -T4, -T451 2014-T6, -T651	2.800	0.1012	950-1180	50 34 40	0.46 0.32 0.37
2017-O 2017-T4, -T451	2.791	0.1008	955-1185	50 34	0.46 0.32
2024-O 2024-T3, -T36, -T4 2024-T6, -T81, -T86	2.781	0.1005	935-1180	50 30 38	0.46 0.29 0.36

See footnotes on page 95.

TYPICAL PHYSICAL PROPERTIES/Wrought Products

Table 4 (continued)

Alloy and Temper	Density at 20°C [3]		Melting Range, approximate °F	Electrical Conductivity at 20°C (68°F), Percent of International Annealed Copper Standard	Thermal Conductivity at 25°C (77°F), CGS units [1]
	g/cm³	lb/cu in.			
2025-T6	2.805	0.1013	970-1185	40	0.37
2117-T4	2.751	0.0994	1080-1200	40	0.37
2218-T72	2.802	0.1012	990-1175	40	0.37
2219-O 2219-T31, -T37 2219-T62, -T81, -T87	2.832	0.1023	1010-1190	44 28 32	0.41 0.27 0.30
2618-T61	2.764	0.0999	1040-1185	39	0.36
3002-O	2.704	0.0977	1195-1215	62 [2]	0.42 [2]
3003-O	2.735	0.0988	1190-1210	46	0.56
3004-O, -H38	2.719	0.0982	1165-1210	42 [2]	0.39 [2]
3005-O, -H12, -H14	2.730	0.0986	1180-1215	....	....
3105-H14, -H16, -H25	2.716	0.0981	1180-1215	45	0.41
4032-O 4032-T6	2.674	0.0966	990-1060	40 35	0.37 0.33
4043-O, -H19	2.685	0.0970	1065-1170	42 [2]	0.39 [2]
5005-O, -H38	2.697	0.0974	1170-1210	54 [2][4]	0.49 [2][4]
5050-O, -H38	2.688	0.0971	1155-1205	50 [2]	0.46 [2]
5052-O, -H38	2.676	0.0967	1125-1200	35 [2]	0.33 [2]
5056-O, -H38	2.642	0.0954	1055-1180	29 [2]	0.28 [2]
5083-O, -H343	2.660	0.0961	1075-1185	29 [2]	0.28 [2]
5086-O, -H34	2.662	0.0962	1085-1185	32 [2]	0.30 [2]

See footnotes on page 95.

TYPICAL PHYSICAL PROPERTIES/Wrought Products

Table 4 (continued)

Alloy and Temper	Density at 20°C③		Melting Range, approximate °F	Electrical Conductivity at 20°C (68°F), Percent of International Annealed Copper Standard	Thermal Conductivity at 25°C (77°F), CGS units ①
	g/cm³	lb/cu in.			
5154-O, -H38	2.662	0.0962	1100-1190	32②	0.30②
5252-H25, -H28	2.699	0.0964	1125-1200	....	.....
5257-H25, -H28	2.696	0.0974	1185-1215	...	...
5356-O	2.643	0.0955	1060-1180	29	0.28
5357-O, -H28	2.694	0.0973	1165-1210	43②	0.40②
5405-H25	2.689	0.0971	1190-1215	56②	0.51②
5454-O, -H34	2.683	0.0969	1115-1195	34②	0.32②
5456-O, -H343	2.652	0.0958	1055-1180	29②	0.28②
5457-O, -H28	2.694	0.0973	1165-1210	46②	0.42②
5557-O, -H28	2.968	0.0975	1180-1215	49②	0.45②
5657-H25, -H28	2.691	0.0972	1175-1210	...	...
6053-O, -T5 6053-T4, -T451 6053-T6, -T651	2.690	0.0972	1100-1205	45 40 42	0.41 0.37 0.39
6061-O 6061-T4, -T451 6061-T6, -T651	2.702	0.0976	1100-1205	47 40 43	0.43 0.37 0.40
6063-O 6063-T1 6063-T5 6063-T6, -T83	2.694	0.0973	1140-1210	58 50 55 53	0.52 0.46 0.50 0.48
6070-O 6070-T4, -T4511 6070-T6, -T6511	2.708	0.0978	1070-1200	52 40 44	0.47 0.37 0.41

See footnotes on following page.

TYPICAL PHYSICAL PROPERTIES/Wrought Products

Table 4 (concluded)

Alloy and Temper	Density at 20°C [3]		Melting Range, approximate °F	Electrical Conductivity at 20°C (68°F), Percent of International Annealed Copper Standard	Thermal Conductivity at 25°C (77°F), CGS units [1]
	g/cm³	lb/cu in.			
6071-O				51	0.47
6071-T4, -T451	2.701	0.0976	1055-1195	39	0.36
6071-T6, -T651				43	0.40
6151-O				54	0.49
6151-T4	2.704	0.0977	1090-1200	42	0.39
6151-T6				45	0.41
6201-T81	2.691	0.0972	1130-1205	54	0.49
6262-T9, -T651	2.719	0.0982	1100-1205	44	0.41
6463-O				58	0.52
6463-T1	2.693	0.0973	1140-1210	50	0.46
6463-T5				55	0.50
6463-T6				53	0.48
6951-O	2.703	0.0977	1140-1210	…	…
6951-T6					
7001-T6	2.837	0.1025	890-1160	31	0.29
7072-O	2.720	0.0983	1195-1215	59	0.53
7075-O				45	0.41
7075-T6, -T651	2.803	0.1013	890-1175	33	0.31
7075-T73, -T7351				39	0.36
7079-T6, -T651	2.750	0.0993	900-1180	32	0.30
7178-T6, -T651	2.829	0.1022	890-1165	31	0.30
8001-O, -H18	2.731	0.0987	1175-1210	58[2]	0.52
8280-O, -H12	2.838	0.1025	440-1175	…	…

[1] CGS unit = cal/cm²/sec/cm/°C. English unit = Btu/ft²/hr/ft/°F. Multiply CGS units by 241.9 to convert to English units.
[2] Average for range.
[3] Computed, using typical composition.
[4] When fabricated for use as electrical conductors, average values for electrical conductivity of the -O and -H19 tempers are 56 and 55 percent respectively, and the corresponding values for thermal conductivities are 0.51 and 0.50.

Percent of Alloying Elements—Aluminum and Normal Impurities Constitute Remainder

Alloy	Silicon	Copper	Manganese	Magnesium	Chromium	Nickel	Zinc	Lead	Bismuth
EC				99.60 percent minimum aluminum					
1060				99.60 percent minimum aluminum					
1100				99.00 percent minimum aluminum					
1145				99.45 percent minimum aluminum					
1180				99.80 percent minimum aluminum					
1188				99.88 percent minimum aluminum					
1199				99.99 percent minimum aluminum					
2EC	0.40	...	...	0.6	...	...	...	...	...
2011	...	5.5	...	...	...	...	...	0.50	0.50
2014	0.8	4.4	0.8	0.50	...	...	...	...	...
2017	...	4.0	0.50	0.50	...	...	...	...	...
2024	...	4.5	0.6	1.5	...	...	...	...	...
2025	0.8	4.5	0.8	...	...	...	...	...	...
2117	...	2.5	...	0.30	...	...	...	...	...
2218	...	4.0	...	1.50	...	2.0	...	...	...
2219②	...	6.3	0.30	...	...	...	...	...	...
2618③	...	2.3	...	1.5	...	1.0	...	...	...
3003	...	...	1.2	...	...	...	...	...	...
3004	...	...	1.2	1.0	...	...	...	...	...
3005	...	...	1.2	0.4	...	...	...	...	...
3105	...	...	0.6	0.50	...	...	...	...	...
4032	12.2	0.9	...	1.1	...	0.9	...	...	...
4043	5.0	...	...	...	...	...	...	...	...
5005	...	...	...	0.8	...	...	...	...	...
5050	...	...	...	1.4	...	...	...	...	...
5052	...	...	...	2.5	0.25	...	...	...	...
5056	...	...	0.10	5.2	0.10	...	...	...	...
5083	...	...	0.8	4.45	0.10	...	...	...	...
5086	...	...	0.45	4.0	0.10	...	...	...	...
5154	...	...	...	3.5	0.25	...	...	...	...
5252	...	...	...	2.5	...	...	...	...	...
5257	...	...	...	0.4	...	...	...	...	...
5356①	...	...	0.10	5.0	0.10	...	...	...	...
5357	...	...	0.30	1.0	...	...	...	...	...
5454	...	...	0.8	2.75	0.10	...	...	...	...
5456	...	...	0.8	5.25	0.10	...	...	...	...
5457	...	...	0.30	1.0	...	...	...	...	...
5554①	...	...	0.8	2.8	0.10	...	...	...	...
5556①	...	...	0.8	5.25	0.10	...	...	...	...
5557	...	...	0.25	0.6	...	...	...	...	...
5657	...	...	...	0.8	...	...	...	...	...
6053	0.7	...	...	1.3	0.25	...	...	...	...
6061	0.6	0.25	...	1.0	0.20	...	...	...	...
6063	0.40	...	...	0.7	...	...	...	...	...
6066	1.3	0.9	0.9	1.1	...	...	...	...	...
6070	1.4	0.3	0.7	0.8	...	...	...	...	...
6071	1.5	0.3	0.7	1.1	...	...	...	...	...

See footnotes on following page.

Alloy	Percent of Alloying Elements—Aluminum and Normal Impurities Constitute Remainder								
	Silicon	Copper	Manganese	Magnesium	Chromium	Nickel	Zinc	Lead	Bismuth
6151	1.0	...	...	0.6	0.25	...	...	...	...
6201	0.7	...	...	0.8	...	...	...	...	...
6262	0.6	0.25	...	1.0	0.09	...	...	0.50	0.50
6463	0.40	...	...	0.7	...	...	...	...	...
6951	0.30	0.25	...	0.6	...	...	...	...	...
7001	...	2.1	...	3.0	0.30	...	7.4	...	...
7072	...	...	...	...	...	...	1.0	...	...
7075	...	1.6	...	2.5	0.30	...	5.6	...	...
8001⑤	...	0.6	...	...	...	...	...	...	...
7079	...	0.6	0.20	3.3	0.20	...	4.3	...	...
7178	...	2.0	...	2.7	0.30	...	6.8	...	...
7277	...	1.25	...	2.0	0.25	...	4.0	...	...
8280④	1.5	1.0	...	...	...	0.5	...	...	...

①Nominal Titanium content—0.10 percent.
②Titanium 0.06; Vanadium 0.10; Zirconium 0.18.
③Iron 1.1; Titanium 0.07.
④Tin 6.2.
⑤Nickel 1.1.

Permanent Mold Castings

Alloy and Temper	Specific Gravity[2]	Weight, lb per cu in.[2]	Approximate Melting Range, °F	Electrical Conductivity[5]	Thermal Conductivity at 25°C CGS units[8]
43-F 43 annealed[4]	} 2.69	0.097	1065-1170	{ 37 42	{ 0.35 0.39
108-F 108 annealed[4] A108-F[1]	} 2.79 2.79	0.101 0.101	970-1160 970-1135	{ 31 38 37	{ 0.30 0.36 0.35
A132-T551[4] F132-T5[1]	2.72 2.76	0.098 0.100	1000-1050 970-1080	29 26	0.28 0.25
138-F[1]	2.95	0.107	945-1110	25	0.25
A140-F	2.78	0.100	955-1120	. .	. . .
142-T21 142-T571[1] 142-T61[1] 142-T77 A142-T75	} 2.81 2.81	0.102 0.102	990-1175 990-1175	{ 44 34 33 38 . .	{ 0.41 0.32 0.31 0.36 . . .
195-T4 195-T62	} 2.81	0.102	970-1190	{ 35 35	{ 0.33 0.33
214-F A214-F[1] F214-F	2.65 2.68 2.66	0.096 0.097 0.096	1110-1185 1075-1180 1090-1185	35 34 36	0.33 0.32 0.34
220-T4	2.57	0.093	840-1120	21	0.21
319-F	2.79	0.101	960-1120	27	0.26
333-F[1] 333-T5[1] 333-T6[1] 333-T7[1]	} 2.77	0.100	960-1085	{ 26 29 29 35	{ 0.25 0.28 0.28 0.33
344-F	2.68	0.097	1065-1145	. .	. . .
354-T61	2.71	0.098	1000-1105	32	0.30
355-T51 355-T6 355-T6[1] 355-T61 355-T7 A355-T51 C355-T61	} 2.71 2.74 2.71	0.098 0.099 0.098	1015-1150 1000-1145 1015-1150	{ 43 36 39 37 42 32 39	{ 0.40 0.34 0.36 0.35 0.39 0.30 0.36
356-T51 356-T6 356-T6[1] 356-T7 A356-T61	} 2.68 2.67	0.097 0.097	1035-1135 1035-1135	{ 43 39 41 40 39	{ 0.40 0.36 0.38 0.37 0.36
A357-T61	2.67	0.096	1035-1135	39	0.36

See following page for footnotes.

Permanent Mold Castings

Alloy and Temper	Specific Gravity②	Weight, lb per cu in.②	Approximate Melting Range, °F	Electrical Conductivity⑤	Thermal Conductivity at 25°C CGS units③
359-T61	2.67	0.097	1045-1115	35	0.33
A612-F	2.81	0.102	1105-1195	35	0.33
C612-F①	2.84	0.103	1120-1190	40	0.37
D612-F	2.81	0.100	1135-1200	25	0.25
750-T5①	2.88	0.104	435-1200	47	0.43
A750-T5①	2.83	0.102	440-1165	43	0.40
B750-T5①	2.88	0.104	400-1175	45	0.41

Die Castings

Alloy	Specific Gravity②	Weight lb per cu in.②	Approximate Melting Range, °F	Electrical Conductivity⑤	Thermal Conductivity at 25°C, CGS units③
13	2.65	0.096	1065-1080	31	0.30
43	2.69	0.097	1065-1170	37	0.35
A214	2.68	0.097	1075-1180	34	0.32
218	2.57	0.093	995-1150	24	0.24
360	2.64	0.095	1035-1105	28	0.27
A360	2.63	0.095	1035-1105	30	0.29
364	2.63	0.095	1035-1115	30	0.29
380	2.72	0.098	1000-1100	23	0.23
A380	2.71	0.098	1000-1100	25	0.25

①Chill cast samples; all other samples cast in green-sand molds.

②The specific gravity and weight data in this table assume solid (void-free) metal. Since some porosity cannot be avoided in commercial castings, their specific gravity or weight will be slightly less than the theoretical value.

③CGS unit = cal/cm²/sec/cm/°C.
English unit = Btu/ft²/hr/ft/°F.
Multiply CGS units by 241.9 to convert to English units.

④While castings are not commonly annealed, similar effects on conductivities may result from the slower rate of cooling of thick sections as compared with thin ones and other variables in foundry practices. Comparison of the values for as-cast and annealed specimens will show the extent to which variations may be expected, depending upon differences in thermal conditions in the production of different types of castings.

⑤Percent of International Annealed Copper Standard, volume basis.

| Alloy | Types of Castings | | | Percent of Alloying Elements—Aluminum and Normal Impurities Constitute Remainder | | | | | | |
	Sand	Permanent Mold	Die	Silicon	Copper	Manganese	Magnesium	Nickel	Zinc	Tin
13			✓	12.0						
43	✓	✓	✓	5.0						
108	✓			3.0	4.0					
A108		✓		5.5	4.5					
A132		✓		12.0	1.0		1.0	2.5		
F132		✓		9.5	3.0		1.0			
138		✓		4.0	10.0		0.30			
A140	✓				8.0	0.50	6.0	0.50		
142	✓	✓			4.0		1.5	2.0		
A142	✓				4.1	②	1.5	2.0		
195	✓			0.8	4.5					
214	✓						4.0			
A214		✓	✓				4.0		1.8	
F214	✓			0.50			4.0			
218			✓				8.0			
220	✓						10.0			
319	✓			6.0	3.5					
333		✓		9.0	3.5					
344		✓		7.0						
354		✓		9.0	1.8		0.50			
355	✓	✓		5.0	1.3		0.50			
A355	✓			5.0	1.4	0.8	0.50	0.8		
C355		✓		5.0	1.3		0.50			
356	✓	✓		7.0			0.30			
A356	✓	✓		7.0			0.30			
A357		✓		7.0		③	0.50			
359		✓		9.0			0.6			
360			✓	9.5			0.50			
A360			✓							
364			✓	8.5		①	0.30			
380			✓	9.0	3.5					
A380			✓							
A612	✓				0.50		0.7		6.5	
C612		✓			0.50		0.35		6.5	
D612	✓					④	0.6		5.8	
750	✓	✓			1.0			1.0		6.5
A750	✓	✓		2.5	1.0			0.50		6.5
B750	✓	✓			2.0		0.75	1.2		6.5

① Also contains 0.35 percent chromium and 0.03 percent beryllium.
② Also contains 0.20 percent chromium.
③ Also contains 0.05 percent beryllium.
④ Also contains 0.50 percent chromium.

Chapter 9

BIBLIOGRAPHY

Adhesion—1963, A.S.T.M. Special Technical Publication No. 360.

Bodner, M.J., ed., *Structural Adhesive Bonding.* (Proceedings of a Symposium held September 14-16, 1965 at Stevens Institute, Hoboken, N.J.) Interscience, New York, to be published.

DeBruyne, N.A., *Research,* Vol. 6, p. 362, London, 1963.

Epstein, G., *Adhesive Bonding of Metals,* Reinhold, New York, N.Y., 1954.

Guttmann, W.H., *Concise Guide to Structural Adhesives,* Reinhold, New York, N.Y., 1961.

Houwink, R., and Salomon, G., *Adhesion and Adhesives,* Elsevier, Amsterdam, New York, 1965.

Katz, I., *Adhesive Materials,* Foster, Long Beach, Calif., 1964.

McGuire, E. Patrick, *American Adhesive Index,* Padric, Mountainside, N.J., 1962.

McGuire, E. Patrick, *Adhesive Raw Materials Handbook,* Padric, Mountainside, N.J., 1964.

Miller, M.A. *Adhesives Age,* Vol. 3, p. 28, March 1960.

Skeist, I., *Handbook of Adhesives,* Reinhold, New York, N.Y., 1962.

Zisman, W.A., *Industrial and Engineering Chemistry,* Vol. 55, p. 18, October 1963.

Alcoa Products and Services

INGOTS

Aluminizing Ingot

Deoxidizing Ingot
  D-OX-IT Shot
  Granulated
  Notch-Bar

Fabricating Ingot
  Extrusion
  Forging
  Sheet
  Wire Bar

Remelt Ingot
  Casting Alloy
  Electrical
    Conductor
    and Rotor Alloy
  Rich Alloy
  Unalloyed

WIRE, ROD AND BAR

Alcoa produces the most complete line of aluminum wire, rod, bar and rolled structurals.

Bar — square, rectangular, hexagonal, cold-finished, special-shaped

Rod — brazing, redraw, cold-finished, special

Screw Machine Stock — round, hexagonal, hollow

Mechanical Tube

Forging Stock — round, square, rectangular

Wire — round, flat, all forms and sizes

SHEET AND PLATE

Sheet available in all lengths, widths and tempers available in commercial alloys. Sheet available in coils, flat, circles, shapes, rings, blanks and tapered sheet.

Plate available in circles, rings, special shapes, rolling slabs and tapered plate.

Special sheet products include:
  Anoclad® Sheet
  Alumilite* Sheet
  Boral Sheet (for atomic applications)
  Brazing Sheet
  Closure Sheet
  Corrugated Sheet
  Duranel® Sheet (stainless-clad aluminum for cooking utensils)
  Fin Stock
  Industrial and Rural Roofing and Siding
  Key Stock
  Lighting Sheet (specular and diffuse finishes)
  Litho Sheet
  Mobile Home Sheet
  Patterned Sheet

*Trade Name of Aluminum Company of America

SHEET AND PLATE — Continued

Painted Sheet (coiled, flat and corrugated)
Porcelain-Enameling Sheet
Recording Sheet Circles
Reflector Sheet
Rigid Container Sheet
Trailer Roof and Panel Sheet
Vinyl-Laminated Sheet (both polyvinyl chloride and polyvinyl fluoride films available)
Patterned and
  Abrasive Armor
  Plate
Reflector Plate
Tooling Plate
Tread Plate

Plate includes;
  Anoclad Plate
  Boral Plate
  (for atomic
  applications)
  Bearing Plate

Modern rolling facilities throughout the country for fast delivery.

ELECTRICAL PRODUCTS

Aerial Cable
Aluminum Bus Bar and Conductor
Aluminum Cable — Steel Reinforced (ACSR)
Armor Wire
Borehole Cable
Building Wire and Cable
Cable: Aluminum and Copper
Cable: High and Low Voltage
CATV Cable
Coaxial Cable
Conduit: Aluminum and Steel
Control and Signal Cable
Dredger Cable
Duct Cable
Elevator Cable
Grounding Cable
Hook-up Wire
Instrumentation Cable
Lead-Covered Cable
Lighting Cable
Locomotive Cable
Mining Machine Cable

Missile Cable
Nonmetallic Sheathed Cable
Portable Cord and Cable
Preassembled Pipe Cable
Service Entrance Cable
Shot-Firing Cord
Shovel Cable
Switchboard Wire
Telemetering Cable
Tie Wire
Transmission and Distribution Accessories
Tree Wire
Trimline Primary Distribution System
Twin-Reel Shuttle-Car Cable
Underground Cable
Underground Residential Distribution Cable (URD)
Weatherproof Wire and Cable
Welding Cable

Alcoa Products and Services — Continued

CASTINGS

Die
Permanent-Mold
  (including
    magnesium)
Sand
Semipermanent-Mold
Plaster
Premium-Engineered

Dependable quality and service from the most modern and complete facilities backed by engineering and research.

PASTE, POWDER AND PIGMENT PRODUCTS

Albron® Products   Atomized Powders
Paste and Flake   Pigments
  Powder   Pastes

FORGINGS

Die: Hammer, Press   Hand
Upset   Rolled Rings

Largest sizes available. All-aluminum, magnesium and titanium alloys. Specification quality. Commercial forgings. Prompt quotations and delivery. Plants at Cleveland, Ohio and Vernon, Calif. Also special Alcoa products such as forged disc wheels, forged manhole steps and other forged products.

IMPACT EXTRUSIONS

The Alcoa Impact process basically combines forging and extrusion in a single operation to produce Alcoa Impacts in alloys ranging from strain-hardened to the highest strength heat-treatable alloys. Currently, the approximate size limits are 12 in. in diameter and 60 in. in length.

Alcoa Impact Extrusions
—offer the most efficient use of metallurgically sound metal.

—are generally produced in one operation on high-speed press equipment.

—save machining costs since they have no draft; have close tolerances; and have efficient distribution of metal, very often eliminating a number of machining operations as well as saving metal.

IMPACT EXTRUSIONS — Continued

—tool costs are generally lower than those for comparable processes.

—often eliminate assembly operations by combining several parts into a single piece, offering the engineer designs unique in wrought materials.

—reduce finishing costs because of their exceptionally smooth surface and absence of parting line.

EXTRUSIONS

Quality extrusions from Alcoa-developed alloys. Largest extrusions commercially available for special products. Wide variety of standard extrusions available including:

Angles   I-Beams
Rods   Tees
Bars   Zees
Channels   Special Shapes
H-Beams

Structural shapes are extruded. Special extrusions for all industries and all design purposes.

TUBULAR PRODUCTS
(Extruded or Drawn)

Irrigation Tube   Duotrace® Pipe
Drill Pipe   Unitrace® Pipe
Oval Tube   Unistrength* Pipe
Square Tube   Construction Tube
Rectangular Tube   Mechanical Tube
Streamlined Tube   Hollow Screw
Wave-Guide Tube   Machine Stock
Extruded Tube   Coiled Utilitube®
Drawn Tube   Tube
Welded Tube   Lighting Standard
Coiled Seamless   Tube
  Tube   Heat Exchanger
Pipe, Structural   Tube
  (conduit) and   Hydraulic Tube
  Seamless

FASTENERS AND SCREW MACHINE PRODUCTS

All types and sizes of standard and special fasteners including:

Bolts
  Cap-Head   Economy   Heavy-Series
  Carriage   Hex   Bearing

Alcoa Products and Services — Continued

FASTENERS AND SCREW MACHINE PRODUCTS — Continued

Cotter Pins

Nuts

Cap	Wing	Aircraft, castle
Hex	Aircraft,	Aircraft, shear
Square	plain	"Compression"
	Jam	

Screws

Machine	Cap
Wood	Flattened Thumb
Sheet Metal	Knurled Thumb
Special	Hexagonal Socket

Nails

Plain	Painted

Rivets

Solid	Semitubular
Solid-Shoulder	Semitubular
Cutlery	Shoulder

Washers

Plain	Lock	Finishing

Binding Posts and Screws

Special Fasteners for Every Industry

Available in bright, Alumilite* or painted finishes. Made from strong Alcoa-developed alloys. Standard or special threads, rigid inspection. All types of screw machine and cold-headed products.

PACKAGING AND FOIL

Foil:

Alcoa Wrap—	Insulations Liner
Household	Stock
Capacitor	Lacquered
Cigarette	Laminated
Christmas Tree	Lithographic
Colored	Nameplate
Container	Pie Plate
Converted	Plain
Dairy Closure	Printed
Embossed	Textured
Freezer	

*Trade Name of Aluminum Company of America

Closures:

Drum and Dust	Screw Caps
Cover Caps	Special Closures
Flavor-Lok® RO®	Standard RO
Goldy®	Stericaps
Hidden-Thread	TopSide RO®
Pilferproof RO	Weighing Dishes

Aluminum Containers

Formed Containers	Rigid Container
Rigid Container	Impacts
Sheet	Collapsible Tube
Rigid Container	Slugs
Slugs	Beer Barrels
	Drums

Machines, Sealing (closures) — Sales and Rentals

Machines, Foil-Laminating — Sales and Rentals

Alcoa Foil service includes a complete package design assistance using plain, embossed, textured, laminated and lacquered and printed foil.

CHEMICAL PRODUCTS

Alflake® (chemical reactant)
Aluminum Fluoride Fluo-Flux®
Aluminas
    Activated
    Calcined
    Calcined Low-Soda
    Catalytic
    Chromatographic
    Hydrated
    Pigment-Grade Trihydrated Hydral®
    Tabular (crushed and graded)
    Tabular (balls)

Gallium

Calcium Aluminate Cement
Calcined Dust
Quick Lime

Aluminas for abrasives, ceramic and refractory purposes. Activated aluminas for desiccant and catalytic applications. Hydrated aluminas for subsequent processing.

Alcoa Products and Services — Continued

BUILDING INDUSTRY PRODUCTS

Alply® Panels
Alshade* Sunscreen
Alumalure® Sheet
Coping
Foil for Insulation
Formed Siding (Insulated and Noninsulated)
Industrial Siding and Accessories
Industrial Roofing and Accessories
Corrugated
E-Rib
  Perforated Corrugated
  Ribbed
  V-Beam
Sealants for Roofing and Siding
Rural Roofing
Rural Siding
  Colorib
  Corrugated
  5-V Crimp
  Ribbed

Colorib® Panels
Electrical Wire and Cable
Fasteners
Sol-Dec® Sunscreen
Stair Treads
Thresholds
Vault Frames
Window Sills
Wire and Cable
Soffit
Fascia
Residental Siding
Gravel Stops
Gutters and Downspouts
Handrails and Fittings
Highway Signs and Structures
Bridge-Rail Systems
Guard-Rail Systems
Manhole Steps

MANUFACTURED PRODUCTS

Alcoa makes a wide variety of specially fabricated products for a number of in-

* Trademark of Aluminum Company of America

MANUFACTURED PRODUCTS — Continued

dustries including process, trucking, railroad, defense and building products. These products are available through Alcoa's Sales Offices and include:

Beer Barrels
Bridge-Rail Systems
Extruded Flooring for Trucks and Trailers
Special Farm Gates
Alcoa Forged Disc Truck Wheels
Forged Meathooks
Highway Signs
Loader Beams
Manhole Steps and Rungs and Manhole Covers
Picnic Shelters
Railroad Crossbucks Signs
Rest Rooms and Comfort Stations
Shipping Containers
Special Forged, Cast, Extruded and Rolled Aluminum Products
Special Research and Development Products for Defense Applications
Special Structurals such as Transmission Towers
Stair Treads
Standard and Special Storage Tanks
Structural Assmblies
Telephone Booths
Welding, Brazing and Soldering Products

Most modern fabricating facilities available. Close proximity to Alcoa's research and development facilities.

Sales Offices

ALABAMA
Birmingham, 35223...........P. O. Box 7424A
ARIZONA
Phoenix, 85014
 5045 North 12th Street, Suite 105
ARKANSAS
Little Rock, 72202.....1515 West Seventh Street
CALIFORNIA
Los Angeles, 90017.....1145 Wilshire Boulevard
Oakland, 94608...............1001 46th Street
San Diego, 92103..........2962 Fifth Avenue
San Francisco (Burlingame), 94011
 1840 Ogden Drive
COLORADO
Denver, 80222........1777 South Bellaire Street
CONNECTICUT
Bridgeport, 06606
 Commerce Park, 4695 Main Street
Hartford, 06105..........1049 Asylum Avenue
DELAWARE
Wilmington, 19801
 825 Bank of Delaware Building
DISTRICT OF COLUMBIA
Washington, 20036........1200 Ring Building
FLORIDA
Miami (Hialeah), 33010.....490 Hialeah Drive
Tampa, 33609......4302 Henderson Boulevard
GEORGIA
Atlanta, 30309
 Alcoa Building, 1615 Peachtree Street
IDAHO
Boise, 83705...............1220 Vista Avenue
ILLINOIS
Chicago, 60611
 Equitable Bldg., 401 North Michigan Avenue
Peoria, 61602
 614 Commercial National Bank Building
INDIANA
Fort Wayne, 46807
 2924 South Calhoun Street Building
Indianapolis, 46205......3969 Meadows Drive
Lafayette, 47902...............P. O. Box 500
South Bend, 46637.......51591 U. S. 31 North
IOWA
Davenport, 52801............601 Brady Street
KANSAS
Wichita, 67208................P. O. Box 8107
KENTUCKY
Louisville, 40202..........Mall Office Center,
 400 Sherburne Lane
LOUISIANA
New Orleans, 70130........No. 1 Canal Street
MARYLAND
Baltimore, 21204..305 West Chesapeake Avenue
MASSACHUSETTS
Boston, 02181............Wellesley Office Park
Worcester, 01608............28 Pleasant Street
MICHIGAN
Detroit, 48202........610 New Center Building
Flint, 48502.....904 Mott Foundation Building
Grand Rapids, 49502
 812 Michigan National Bank Building
Jackson, 49201.....310 National Bank Building
MINNESOTA
Minneapolis, 55424......4010 West 65th Street

MISSOURI
Kansas City, 64112.....4601 Madison Avenue
St. Louis, 63105.......8301 Maryland Avenue
NEBRASKA
Omaha, 68102
 646 Omaha National Bank Building
NEW JERSEY
Newark (East Orange), 07018..100 Halsted Street
NEW YORK
Albany, 12206...............40 Colvin Avenue
Buffalo, 14240.................P. O. Box 1065
Garden City (L. I.), 11530
 1001 Franklin Avenue
New York, 10017.............200 Park Avenue
Rochester, 14618..............Erdle Building
Syracuse, 13201..............731 James Street
NORTH CAROLINA
Charlotte, 28204.....1200 East Morehead Street
OHIO
Akron, 44303.........759 West Market Street
Cincinnati, 45206
 Alcoa Building, 2331 Victory Parkway
Cleveland, 44114........One Erieview Plaza
Columbus, 43215.........230 Bryson Building
Dayton, 45405.........207 Northtown Arcade
Toledo (Sylvania), 43560....5800 Monroe Street
Youngstown, 44503...537 Ohio Edison Building
OKLAHOMA
Oklahoma City, 73103....111 N. W. 23rd Street
OREGON
Portland, 97232...............111 Lloyd Plaza
PENNSYLVANIA
Allentown, 18102.......1202 Washington Street
Philadelphia, 19102
 1800 Two Penn Center Plaza
Pittsburgh, 15220.........875 Greentree Road
York, 17401.............25 North Duke Street
TENNESSEE
Chattanooga, 37402....1237 Volunteer Building
Knoxville (Alcoa, Tenn.), 37701....P. O. Box 68
Memphis, 38117...........4515 Poplar Avenue
Nashville, 37215.....235 Wilson-Bates Building
TEXAS
Dallas, 75201.......1900 Fidelity Union Tower
Houston, 77027
 Suite 300, 5050 Westheimer Road
Lubbock, 79405............203 Fields Building
VIRGINIA
Richmond, 23227
 2123 West LaBurnum Avenue
WASHINGTON
Seattle, 98104.............1401 Madison Street
Spokane, 99201..........509 Fidelity Building
WEST VIRGINIA
Charleston, 25301
 Nelson Bldg., 1018 Kanawha Boulevard, East
WISCONSIN
Milwaukee, 53233
 2040 West Wisconsin Avenue
Wausau, 54401...........203½ Fourth Street

NEW YORK EXPORT OFFICE
New York, N. Y., 10017......200 Park Avenue

FOREIGN SALES OFFICES

HONG KONG, B.C.C.
Alcoa International (Asia) Limited
 Luk Hoi Tong Building, 31 Queen's Road Central
KINGSTON, JAMAICA
Alcoa International, Limited.....P. O. Box 516

LAUSANNE, SWITZERLAND
Alcoa International, S.A.....61 Avenue d'Ouchy
TORONTO 2, ONTARIO, CANADA
Alcoa International Canada, Ltd.
 2 Carlton Street, Suite 1704

ALUMINUM COMPANY OF AMERICA

General Offices, 1501 Alcoa Building, Pittsburgh, Pennsylvania 15219

Printed in U.S.A. 6611